THE GREAT MAHABHARATA

SHANTI

SHANTI PUBLICATIONS

492-E/5-A, Mahaveer Block Street No. 5,
Bhola Nath Nagar, Shahdara, Delhi-110032

THE
GREAT
MAHABHARATA

New Edition:-2015

ISBN : 978-81-7920-310-1

Published By:

SHANTI PUBLICATIONS

**492-E/5-A, Mahaveer Block
Street No. 5,
Bhola Nath Nagar, Shahdara
Delhi-110032 (INDIA)
Ph.: 22307950, 22303794
mail at: shantipublications@hotmail.com**

CONTENTS

After composing eighteen tales of the bygone ages of the Hindu mythology (Puranas), Maharishi Vyasa, thought of writing yet another huge book. He wanted somebody to help him to write it. On Lord Brahma's advice, he went to Lord Ganesha and said, "Hey Lord of the Universe! I have decided to write a huge book on the Hindu mythology. But it is very difficult to think and write at the same time. So I would like to request you to please give your writing to my words."

Ganesha said, "Maharishi! I am ready to help you but I will stop writing if I feel disturbed in between."

Maharishi said, "OK. But you must understand and write each stanza carefully". Ganesha agreed.

Long ago in Hastinapur, there ruled a great king named Shantanu. He was a descendent of the Kuru dynasty. There was peace and happiness in his kingdom.

One day, he went hunting in a forest near the river Ganga. While returning, he halted near the river for a while. He sat under a tree to take rest. Just then, he saw a beautiful damsel coming out of the river. She was elegantly walking along the river waves. Overwhelmed by her beauty, King Shantanu was drawn towards her. So he asked, "Hey beauty! Who are you and what are you doing here in isolation?"

The lady answered, "Why are you asking this? I don't even know you."

I am Shantanu, the king of Hastinapur. I have never

seen anyone as beautiful as you before. I fell in love with you the moment I saw you," the king said.

"Will you marry me," asked the beauty. "Why not?" replied King Shantanu.

"I agree with your proposal, but on one condition," said the lady. "I am Ganga, the Goddess of this holy river. My condition is that you will never question me or stop me in whatever I do. The moment you break this promise, I will leave you for ever."

Ganga's condition was very unusual. But King Shantanu was greatly in love with her and wanted to marry her at any cost. So without thinking any further, he accepted her proposal. King Shantanu married Ganga and brought her to the palace. After a few months, she gave birth to a baby boy. King Shantanu was overjoyed with the news. When he

was coming to see his child, he saw Ganga going towards the river. He followed her. He saw the queen setting afloat the child in the river. King Shantanu was very unhappy at Ganga's cruelty but since he was bound with the promise, he kept quiet. In this way, Ganga set afloat her seven sons, one after the other.

But when she was taking her eighth son, the King lost his patience and asked, "What kind of mother are you? You kill your own children! What makes you do such a cruel act? Aren't you ashamed of it?"

Listening to the king, Ganga stopped and said, "OK, king! I will not drown this child. He will be your progeny. But since you have broken your promise, I cannot stay here anymore. I am going."

RETURN OF DEVAVRATA

King Shantanu was very unhappy because Ganga was leaving him for ever. Ganga condoled him and said, "King! Don't be so upset. Everything was set before by our destiny. My coming on Earth and our marriage were all set beforehand for a purpose. Now since the work is over, I must leave now." King Shantanu was shocked. He asked, "Ganga! Please explain me everything in detail."

Ganga said, "Once Guru Vashishtha was deep in meditation. Just then eight Vasus, the vedic gods, disturbed him. He became furious and cursed them, "You all have made fun of an ascetic practice. So you will have to take birth as human beings to face all the mental and physical torments on the earth."

All the Vasus apologised and requested him to take back his curse. Guru Vashishtha felt sorry for the Vasus and said, "I cannot withdraw my curse, but seven of you will die as soon as you take birth on the earth and then return back to heaven."

Among all the Vasus, the eighth one did not feel sorry for his rudeness. Guru Vashishtha said, "You are not ashamed of your bad behaviour. So, you will have to suffer this curse. That is why, it will fall upon you only."

"So, this is the eighth Vasu now. You have saved him by breaking your promise. Now I am leaving for the heaven. I am taking your son with me because I want to see him grow under my supervision. When time comes, I will return him back to you." Saying this, she concentrated herself into the river water with the baby.

King Shantanu returned back with a heavy heart. Years went by, he was anxiously waiting for his son's return. One day, he saw a very attractive boy standing near the river. King Shantanu was drawn towards the boy. Suddenly, Ganga came out of the river. She held the boy's hand and took him to the king and said, "King! this is your eighth son, Devavrata. This boy is blessed with a long life and will serve you for ever. He is very powerful and strong."

King Shantanu was very pleased to see his son. After handing over his son to him, Ganga once again concentrated into the river water. The king was happy to find his son. There was a grand celebration in the city.Devavrata was declared the Prince of Hastinapur.

BHISHMA AND HIS PROMISE

King Shantanu was proud to have a son like Devavrata. But, he could never forget Ganga. Once, while returning back from the

forest, he felt very tired. He halted for a while on the riverbank. Just then, he saw a beautiful lady sitting in a boat. King Shantanu went close to her and asked, "Hey Beauty! Who are you and why are you sitting on this boat?"

The lady said, "I am Satyavati. My father is a fisherman. I take people to the other side of the river."

Attracted by Satyavati's beauty, King Shantanu proposed to her.

But very politely she replied, "My father will decide for my marriage. So, you must first talk to him."

"Then take me to him. I will ask him for your hand," said the king. So, Satyavati took him to her hut. Her father immediately recognised the king and said, "Sire! Why did you take the pain to come here? You should have sent for me."

King Shantanu said, "I have come to ask for your daughter's hand. I want to marry her."

The fisherman said, "It is my good fortune. I accept your proposal, but on the condition that only my grandson inherits your kingship."

King Shantanu was shocked to hear this. No doubt, he had fallen in love with his daughter, but the condition would be an injustice to his son Devavrata. So, he quietly returned back to Hastinapur.

Back home, Shantanu could not forget Satyavati.

He lost his interest in all his works. Not only this, he neither ate on time, nor he slept well. He was growing very weak day by day.

Devavrata was very upset at his father's condition. He asked him the reason, but not being satisfied with his answer, he discussed the matter with the chief minister. After knowing the truth, he went straight to the fisherman, Satyavati's father.

Devavrata said to the fisherman, "I take a vow that your grandson will be the descendent of Hastinapur. Now, there should not be any objection to the marriage on your behalf."

The fisherman said, "Prince! I have full faith that you will not claim your inheritance. But in future, your son might claim for it. Then what? Imagine

the condition of my daughter and her son then."

Devavrata then deeply thought and came to a conclusion as to what the fisherman actually wanted. He said, "I take a vow by keeping the four directions of the earth as a witness that I will remain a Brahmachari (Bachelor) throughout my life."

After listening to this, Satyavati's father and Devavrata took Satyavati to Hastinapur. King Shantanu was very happy to see Satyavati. But when he came to know about his son's vow, tears rolled down his face. He said, "Devavrata! I am proud of you. You have done what no son has ever done or will ever do for his father. I grant you a boon of death at will. And from today, you will be known as Bhishma." This is how Devavrata got his name, Bhishma.

King Shantanu married Satyavati and begot two sons—Chitrangad and Vichitravirya. But soon, the King passed away. Chitrangad ascended the royal throne of Hastinapur. But unfortunately, he died fighting in a war. After his death, Vichitravirya began to rule the country under Bhishma's guardianship.

Once the king of Kashi organised a svayamvar for his three daughters—Amba, Ambika and Ambalika. Bhishma abducted them to be Vichitravirya's brides. On reaching Hastinapur, Amba told Bhishma that she loves king Shalva and wishes to marry him. So, Bhishma sent her to King Shalva.

Ambika and Ambalika were married to Vichitravirya. Unfortunately, he too died without any heir.

Satyavati was very upset. One day, she went to Bhishma and said, "Son! Now there is no justification in keeping your vow. Both my sons have become a victim of untimely  death. So now, it is your duty to sit on the throne and marry your brother's widows to give a heir."

Very humbly Bhishma replied, "Dear mother! I have no need to break my vow because you have yet another son, Maharshi Vyasa. He can sit on the throne and fulfill your ambition. Now Satyavati remembered, when she was not married, a son was born to her through Sage Parashara.

So, she immediately sent a message to Sage Vyasa. When he reached Hastinapur, Satyavati greeted him and told him the whole story. Maharishi said, "Respected mother! Don't be so upset. Just give me your orders."

When Satyavati asked him to take over Hastinapur's

responsibilities, he said, "If I accept kingship, I will get involved in homely matters and will not be able to complete my spiritual aim."

Maharshi's reasoning was genuine, so the queen did not object him. But she did not lose hope, and said, "OK! I will not come in between your aim, but at least, you can give a progeny to the widows of Vichitravirya to carry on the Kaurava dynasty."

To obey his mother's order, Maharshi decided to stay in the palace. He had a very dark, ugly and fearsome face. When Ambika came to his room, she was scared and fearfully closed her eyes. When Ambika left the room, the sage told the queen, "She will give birth to a blind child."

Next, Satyavati sent Ambalika to the sage's room.

Her face became pale in fear when she saw the fearsome face of the sage. Once she had left, the sage said, "Ambalika's son will be of yellowish complexion."

Satyavati wanted a healthy child for the kingdom. So, she sent an intelligent maid to his room. When the maid left the sage's room, he said, "This lady will give birth to a very intelligent boy."

After a few months, the three pregnant ladies gave birth to three sons. As the sage had predicted, Ambika's son was born blind. He was named "Dhritarashtra". Ambalika's son was born yellowish, so he was named "Pandu". Satyavati's maid gave birth to a healthy son, who was named "Vidura".

Under the guardianship of Bhishma, when they grew up, Pandu ascended the throne and Vidura was made the chief minister of Hastinapur.

KING WEDS GANDHARI

Once Bhishma sent a message to the king of Gandhar. It said, "We propose for marrying Prince Dhritarashtra to your daughter Gandhari."

Although it was a matter of great honour for Gandhar king to receive such a proposal, but since Dhritarashtra was blind, he was feeling uncomfortable to accept it. When Gandhari came to know about her father's hesitation, she said, "Respected father! If it is for his blindness, from today onwards, I will never see this world again."

Saying this, she took a piece of cloth and tied it on her eyes. Gandhari's brother Shakuni took her to Hastinapur, where she got married to Dhritarashtra. The marriage function carried on for a long time.

THE STORY OF KUNTI

Kuntibhoja was childless. So, he adopted the daughter of Bhusena and named her Kunti. Once Sage Durvasa came to meet Kuntibhoja. Kunti served him whole-heartedly. The sage granted her a boon that she could call any God to acquire a son from him.

One day, Kunti was worshipping the sun God on the riverbank. Just then, she remembered sage Durvasa's boon. She wanted to testify it. She began to recite the mantra to summon the sun God. The God appeared before her and said, "You have called me, so I grant you a glorious son." So with the blessings of the sun God, Kunti acquired a son.

Kunti felt embarrassed when she acquired a son as she was unmarried. Being unmarried she could not take the baby home, so, she kept the child in a basket and set it afloat in the river. After this, she returned back to the palace.

On the other side of the river, Adhirath, a charioteer of the king, and his wife Radha were worshipping the sun God. Just then, they saw a basket floating in the river. They got excited and picked up the basket. Adhirath and his wife were overjoyed to see the newborn in the basket. Since they were childless, they took the baby home. They named him 'Radhey'. In this way, the boy at first was known as Radhey but later on, he became very famous as 'Karna'.

PANDU IS CURSED

After the marriage of Dhritarashtra, Bhishma sent King Pandu's marriage proposal to King Kuntibhoja, for his daughter Kunti, and King Shalya of Bhadra, for his daughter Maadri. Both the kings accepted it. Both Kunti and Maadri were married to King Pandu with great pomp and show.

Once Pandu, with his wives, went towards the Himalayas. One day while roaming about, he sighted a beautiful pair of deers. Without a second thought, he set his bow towards it. In fact, Sage Kindum and his wife had taken the form of deers. As the arrow struck them, they came to their real form. The sage cursed the king, "You have committed a big sin by killing us. So whenever you try to go near your wife, you will die."

Cursed Pandu decided to do ascetic practice. He asked his wives to return back to the palace, but they decided to stay there with their husband.

One day, when Pandu was engrossed in his ascetic practice, a sage saw him and said, "You are no doubt practising hard, but in order to get oneself freed from their debts, it is necessary to beget a son. May God help you to acquire sons from the Gods, through both your queens.

Pandu was overjoyed with such blessings. He said to Kunti, "You don't know, you can save me from a big dilemma. Without any delay, you worship Dharamraj, Vayudeva and Indradeva for a son each."

Kunti, following her husband's order, acquired a son each from the three Gods. They were named as Yudhishthira, Bhima and Arjuna.

When Madri saw Kunti with her sons, her feeling of maternity developed. She told Pandu about her desire. King Pandu then asked Kunti to teach the mantra to Madri. Madri worshipped God Ashwini Kumar and acquired twins—Nakula and Sahdeva. In this way, Pandu got five brave sons, who later on came to be known as Pandavas.

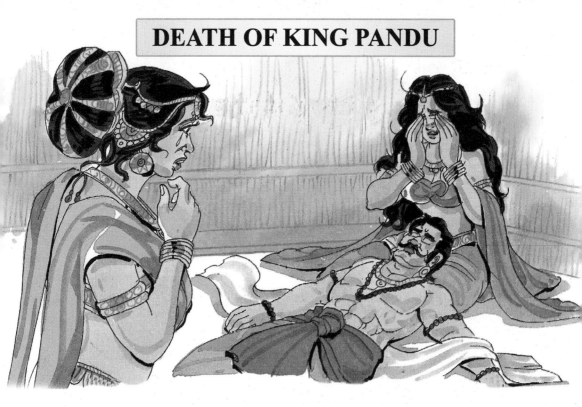

King Pandu, with his two wives and children, was happily spending his life in the Vanaprastha ashram.

One day finding Madri alone, Pandu tried to embrace her. Madri tried to make him aware of Sage Kandum's curse. But Pandu was not ready to listen to her. He was enamoured by Madri. No sooner he embraced Madri, he fell on the ground and died. Madri began to cry aloud. Listening to the cry, Kunti came running into the hut. She was shocked to see Pandu lying dead. Kunti too started crying clinging to her husband's dead body.

Both the queens wanted to perform sati alongwith their husband. But the sages present there condoled

them and said, "If both of you become sati, your children will become orphans. Who will take care of these little children?"

After this Madri said to Kunti, "Sister! You are my elder with a huge heart. So please take the responsibility of the children and allow me to perform sati with my husband."

For the sake of the five Pandavas, Kunti had to change her decision, while Madri became sati with king Pandu.

The sages then advised Kunti to return back to Hastinapur with the children. Thus, Kunti returned back to the palace with the Pandavas.

THE ENEMITY

Since King Pandu did not return back for a long time, Dhritarashtra became the ruler of Hastinapur. He had 100 sons, who were called Kauravas. His eldest sons, Duryodhana and Dusshasana, were under the guardianship of their maternal uncle, Shakuni, who was very sly. He had developed a wrong concept that since Dhritarashtra was blind, and Pandavas were not there, Duryodhana was the real inheritor of the kingdom, not Pandavas.

As such, Duryodhana was not ready to handover Hastinapur to the Pandavas at any cost. He envied Bhima the most because the latter was more powerful and stronger than him. With several

qualities, Bhima had one bad habit that he ate a lot. Duryodhana tried to take advantage of this habit.

One day, he planned to walk along the riverbank with the Pandavas. He had brought laddoos. He poisoned two of these and gave them to Bhima. After eating them, Bhima fell sick. Duryodhana then pushed him into the river. When everyone returned back to the palace except Bhima, Duryodhana thought that Bhima must have drowned in the Ganga. In fact, where Bhima fell, many poisonous snakes were there. When a snake stung him, his poison disappeared. On feeling better, he swam to the shore. In the palace, mother Kunti and his brothers were happy to see Bhima hale and hearty.

Bhishma was in search of a guru for his grand-children. Once, while playing, their ball fell into a well. The children peeped into it. They saw the ball floating on the water, but were unable to take it out.

Just then, they saw a Brahman meditating under a tree. The children went and stood there watching him. Looking at their dull faces, he asked, "Children! Why are you so upset?" The children replied, "Hey Brahman! Our ball has fallen in the well, and we are unable to take it out. Could you help us?"

The Brahman said, "All of you should be ashamed of yourself as you come from a Kshatriya family and cannot even take a ball out of the well."

The children had no answer to the sage's comment and so, they hung their heads in shame.

Next, the Brahman went near the well and aimed his arrow towards the ball. The arrow struck the ball. Then he shot his arrows one after the other, in a row. He kept on shooting the arrows, until the last arrow reached the top of the well. Then, he went forward and pulled out the arrow with the ball from the well.

The little princes were overwhelmed by the Brahman's archery. When they requested him to teach them this art, he replied, "OK! But first go and ask your grandfather Bhishma if he allows."

The children went straight to Bhishma and told him the matter. Bhishma knew that the Brahman could

be nobody else but Dronacharya. On his request, Guru Dronacharya began to teach the children the art of weaponry.

One day, when the little princes found him gloomy, they said, "Gurudev! You seem to be very depressed. Can we know the reason?"

Dronacharya replied, "When time allows, I will surely tell you the reason. Right now, I want all of you to make a promise to me." All the princes kept quiet, but Arjuna went forward and said, "I promise to do whatever you say."

Dronacharya became very pleased. He blessed him and said, "Arjuna! I am proud to have a pupil like you." Tears of happiness rolled down from his face. From that day, Arjuna became his best and beloved pupil.

PRINCES TAKE AN EXAM

The first level of weaponry was over. Now, Guru Dronacharya decided to test his pupil.

In order to test the pupils' ability in archery, he hung a wooden bird on the branch of a tree. He then said, "Children! Each of you will get one chance. Whoever pierces the right eye of the bird will be the best archer."

First, he asked Yudhishthira to aim at the bird. Yudhishthira began to aim for the bird's eye. Just then Guru Drona asked him, "Yudhishthira! What do you see?"

He replied, "Guruji! A tree, bird and leaves."

"Then you will not be able to aim. Go back," Drona said.

After this, he asked the same question to the other three Pandavas, one after the other. But none of them gave him the right answer.

At the end, Guru Drona asked Arjuna the same question. He replied, "Guruji! I see the right eye of the bird only."

Dronacharya was very impressed by Arjuna's answer. He asked him to aim at the bird. Arjuna pierced the right eye of the bird. Guru Drona declared him the best archer.

THE STORY OF EKLAVYA

Whenever Eklavya, a Bheel boy passed through the ashram, he watched the princes learning archery. One day he went in and said, "Guruji! Will you make me your pupil?" Guru Drona said, "No, I teach children of royal families only. So, look for some other guru."

Dronacharya's refusal depressed Eklavya, but he did not lose hope. He carved a statue of Dronacharya and began to practise archery.

One day, when Eklavya was practising archery, a barking dog broke his concentration. In order to make the dog quiet, he shot a number of arrows towards the dog. It made the dog stop barking.

Guru Dronacharya was surprised to see the dog with stitched mouth. He said, "It must be a job of a great archer. Let's go and find him out."

Saying this, Guru Dronacharya left the ashram with some of his pupils in search of this great archer. Soon, they reached at the place where Eklavya was busy practising. When Dronacharya saw his own statue, and Eklavya practising in front of it, he was highly impressed by the latter's devotional sentiment and faith. He went close to Eklavya and said, "You are indeed a great archer. I am highly impressed by your strength and devotion towards this art. May I know, who is your guru?" Eklavya saluted him and said, "Sir! You."

"But how?" Dronacharya asked surprisingly. Eklavya pointed towards the statue and said, "I used to do my practice in front of the statue. I have great faith in you. You are my icon."

Guru Drona never wanted any competitor for his favourite student, Arjuna. So he set a very cruel plan and said, "If you have learnt this art from me, pay me the gurudakshina."

Eklavya bowed to him and said, "Order me, Guruji!" "As gurudakshina, give me the thumb of your right hand," said Guru Drona. At once Eklavya cut off the thumb of his right hand! Everyone was shocked to see such a devoted pupil facing a cruel guru.

On the completion of their education in weaponry, a competition was held. Here, all the princes including Kauravas and Pandavas were supposed to show their talents. He tied his eyes with a piece of cloth and shot a Shabdabhedhi arrow on an unseen man, just on hearing a sound made by him. Then, through one arrow, he produced fire, and through another arrow, it began to rain.

The club fight between Bhima and Duryodhana was also very exciting, as both were champions in this art. That is why, this competition between the two became very dangerous. Ashwatthama, Dronacharya's son, came in between and saved the fight.

Karana was unable to stand the victory of Bhima over his friend Duryodhana in the club fight, and the praise of Arjuna in archery. He also desired to show his talent in the competition.

"Why not, Karna! You can also show your talent in archery," said Guru Dronacharya. "But I want you to compete with Arjuna in archery," replied Karna.

Everyone in the palace knew that the competition between the two will also be very fearful. Guru Kripacharya argued, "This competition is only for the princes, therefore, Karna cannot take part in it. He is the son of a charioteer."

Duryodhana found this very insulting for his friend Karna. Therefore, he immediately declared, "I declare Karna as the king of Ang kingdom. So now, my friend Karna can take part in the royal competition." Karna thanked Duryodhana.

REVENGE OF DRONACHARYA

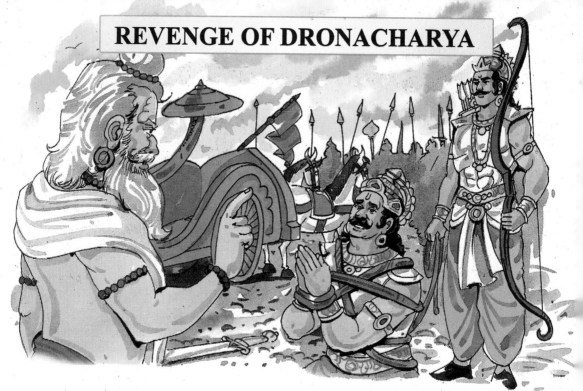

After completion of the education, Guru Drona asked his pupils to make King Drupada a captive, and present before him. This would be a token of his gurudakshina. Arjuna requested him to allow him to do this. So with Drona's permission, Arjuna and his brother attacked Panchal. In the war, the Pandavas captured King Drupada and presented him before Dronacharya.

Dronacharya was very happy to see Drupada as a captive. He said, "Say Drupada! How do you feel now? As the kingdom that you were so proud of is mine now, I am no more poor. Say, am I eligible to be your friend or not?" Drupada felt very ashamed and apologised to him.

Pandavas displayed good behaviour, morality, humbleness and bravery. So, they were very popular.

On the other hand, Duryodhana, from his childhood was very arrogant and had bad intentions. This was because he was always influenced by his uncle Shakuni. Duryodhana always tried out plans to let down the Pandavas. But since Yudhishthira was the eldest son and the most competent person, Bhishma decided to crown him as the prince.

Bhishma praised Yudhishthira's humbleness, patience, truthfulness and impartiality, and desired to crown him the king. Dhritarashtra was not happy to hear this because he wanted his son Duryodhana to become the new crown prince of Hastinapur.

Duryodhana became fretful with the declaration,

but he could not do anything. His maternal uncle
Shakuni and Karna were also very upset with this.
They never wanted the Pandavas to rule over
Hastinapur. They wanted Pandavas to leave
Hastinapur for ever, so Duryodhana was very upset
over Yudhishthira becoming the king.

His father Dhritarashtra was also very upset with
this. But, he pretended to be happy and cooperated
with the Pandavas. Duryodhana became more
fretful and began to make dreadful plans to destroy
the Pandavas. In these evil plans, Shakuni, Karna
and Dusshasana were equally involved.

THE LAKSHAGRIH

Once Duryodhana, Shakuni, Karna and Dusshasana planned to burn Pandavas alive. Shakuni very secretly constructed Lakshagrih, a palace of lac. According to the plan, the Pandavas were asked to attend the festival of Varanavat. With no hesitation, they accepted the invitation. Duryodhana was very glad with Pandavas' decision.

Luckily Vidura, the chief minister of Hastinapur and a well-wisher of the Pandavas, came to know about Duryodhana's evil plans. He got made a tunnel in the Lakshagrih and informed the Pandavas about the plan. Since Vidura had already informed the Pandavas about it, when Lakshagrih was set on fire, they came out through the secret tunnel and reached the riverside.

According to the schedule, the Pandavas reached Varanavat. The people of Varanavat were very glad to see Prince Yudhishthira and his brothers.

It was a seven day festivity. So, on the last day, after the end of the function, the Pandavas reached Lakshagrih. Before the execution of Duryodhana's plan, Bhima set fire in the palace and very quietly crept out through the secret tunnel with mother Kunti and his brothers. Soon, they reached the bank of the river Ganga. A boat was waiting for them here. They boarded the boat and sailed to the other side of the river.

PANDAVAS LIVE IN A JUNGLE

The news of death of the Pandavas spread like forest fire in Hastinapur too. Bhishma, Guru Dronacharya and Guru Kripracharya were very sad. Dhritarashtra and Duryodhana pretended to be sad. But from within, they were glad. Now Duryodhana could easily ascend the throne of Hastinapur.

On the other hand, after crossing the river Ganga, Kunti and her sons reached a dense forest. They were so tired and hungry that they decided to rest under a shady tree. At night, mother Kunti and the four Pandavas went off to sleep, while Bhima remained alert for his family's safety. The king of  that jungle was a giant called Hidimb. His sister Hidimba was roaming about in the forest. She saw Bhima. Through her magical power, she turned into a beautiful lady and went near

him and asked, "Who are you and who are these people sleeping under the tree?" When Bhima did not reply, she said, "I want to marry you. Do you accept my proposal?" Before she could say anything else, her brother Hidimb appeared there.

Soon, a fierce battle began between Bhima and Hidimb. It made mother Kunti and his brothers wake up. Bhima lifted up Hidimb and threw him on the ground. With a huge bang, he died there and then.

Kunti was very proud at her son's bravery. Then, she saw Hidimba standing next to Bhima. Before Kunti could say anything, Hidimba said, "Respected mother! I love your son and desire to marry him." Impressed by her simplicity, Kunti gave her permission. But it was on the condition that she could live freely with Bhima during the day, but at night, she would let him guard his family.

Soon, Bhima and Hidimba got married. Bhima spent the day with his wife Hidimba and at night, he would return to his family. Soon, Hidimba gave birth to a baby boy. They named him Ghatotkachh.

Hidimba had an agreement with Bhima that she would stay with him, until a son is born to them. So now, Hidimba went away with her son. After this incidence, the Pandavas also left the forest.

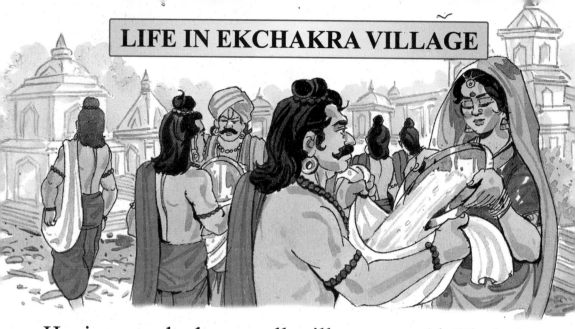

Having reached a small village named Ekchakra, the Pandavas began to live with a Brahman family. They would beg around to fulfill their daily needs. Whatever food they collected from begging, Kunti would divide it into two parts. Kunti and her four sons would eat from one part, while Bhima would get the other part alone.

One day, Kunti heard somebody crying. When she went there, she found that the housekeeper's wife and daughter were crying. Kunti asked, "Why are you crying? May I know the reason? You have given us shelter. So it is also our duty to share your grief. Please say how can we help you?"

The Brahman said, "Sister! Nobody can help us out in our problem. And some day, everyone in this village will have to face this circumstance."

"But still, I want to know the reason for your grief. Maybe, we can help you," said Kunti.

The Brahman said, "A little away from this village, in a cave, there lives a ferocious man-eating giant, named Bakasura. In order to satisfy his hunger, we have to send a man, along with a cart full of food, daily. Today it is our turn. We cannot tolerate the separation of anyone among us."

Kunti said, "None of you but Bhima, my son, will go to the giant today."

"No. You are my guest. How can I send my guest into such a dreadful situation?" replied the Brahman.

"You need not worry. My son will save not only your family, but the whole village by killing the giant," said Kunti confidently.

At the end, the Brahman agreed. Kunti told his sons everything about Bakasura and said that she had decided to send there Bhima, instead of the Brahman.

When Yudhishthira became very thoughtful about it, Bhima assured him that he would surely be able to kill that wicked Bakasura.

So that evening, Bhima, with a cart full of food, went towards the cave. On reaching there, he let open the oxen and began to eat the food himself.

After eating, he called aloud for Bakasura who was waiting for his food. Hearing his name, Bakasura came out of his cave. When he saw the empty cart

and Bhima, he screamed aloud in anger and leapt upon Bhima. Bhima quickly moved and firmly caught both his legs with his hand and overturned him. Then, he dropped him on the ground. Before Bakasura could rise, Bhima stamped hard with his right leg on Bakasura's heart, and killed him.

Then, he tied a rope around the dead giant's neck and hung him on the entrance door of the village, so that the villagers could see that Bakasura is dead. After this, Kunti and her sons left the village.

DRUPADA BEGETS A SON

Once King Drupada invited two sages named "Yajna" and "Upyajna" and told them to perform a yajna for acquiring a heir.

When the yajna was over, the sages asked the queen to come and take the food offered in the yajna. But she asked the sages to wait. This angered the sages and they threw the food into the holy fire. Just then, a very strong and handsome man emerged out of the fire. The sages handed him to King Drupada. He named him Dristdyuman.

King Drupada also had a beautiful, marriageable daughter, Draupadi. He organised a swayamvar for her, in which he invited not only the princes, but also Brahmans and sages from far off places.

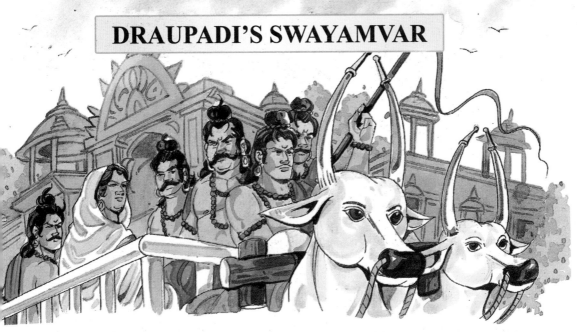

DRAUPADI'S SWAYAMVAR

King Drupada made a huge bow for Draupadi's swayamvar. It was kept hanging and it had a wood fish hung in the middle. Just below it, there was a big cauldron filled with oil. A contestant had to see the shadow of the fish in the oil and then aim for the eyes of the fish.

When the Pandavas came to know about this swayamvar, they came to attend it as Brahmans. Shri Krishna was also present in the function. He wanted Draupadi to marry Arjuna.

Many brave princes were present in the swayamvar. Each one of them tried their luck, but none of them succeeded. At the end, Karna came forward. No sooner had he lifted the bow, Draupadi interrupted and said, "Before taking part, please introduce

yourself. As far as I know, you are a charioteer's son. So, you cannot participate in this swayamvar."

Whatever Draupadi said was true. But Duryodhana could not tolerate it. He stood up and said, "O Princess! You have insulted my friend. He is the king of Anga, so you must apologize to him." Duryodhana's statement had no effect on Draupadi. She said, "Prince of Hastinapur! I agree that he is your friend, but still he does not belong to a princely family. Charity never makes a man a king. So, I refuse to marry him."

After this Karna and Duryodhana immediately left the swayamvar. Just then, Arjuna, as a Brahman, walked towards the swayamvar venue. There was a commotion among the Brahmans present there. Some of them said, "Stop him. He will ruin all our reputation. When great archers could not succeed, how can this Brahman do it?"

Arjuna did not care. He lifted the bow and arrow, aimed at the shadow of the fish and pierced its eyes. A commotion developed among the people present there. Krishna had already informed King Drupad and Draupadi about Arjuna, so they were very happy about it. But the other princes present there objected to this marriage and ran to beat King Drupad. But before they could do any foolishness, the Pandavas came forward to take Draupadi home.

Reaching their house, they called aloud for their mother and said, "Look what we have brought today."

Kunti was busy worshipping, so she simply said, "OK. Equally distribute it among yourselves." But when she opened her eyes, she was surprised to see a bride. She regretted her words.

Draupadi said to Kunti, "Dear Mother! Don't be so thoughtful. Lord Shiva has given me a boon of five brave husbands. So I am your five sons' wife."

Lord Krishna also tried to pacify Kunti and said, "Draupadi, in order to get a husband with five different qualities, had performed a hard ascetic practice, but Lord Shiva gave her a boon to become a wife of five men."

Now Kunti and the Pandavas were satisfied. And Draupadi became the wife of five Pandavas.

When Vidura got the news about the Pandavas' marriage to Draupadi, the Panchala princess, he was overjoyed. He went straight away to Dhritarashtra with the news. He said, "Maharaj! There is news from Panchala, that the Pandavas are alive. The person who has won Draupadi in her Swayamvar is none, but Arjuna."

Dhritarashtra was shocked, but he pretended to be very glad. He said, "This is indeed a precious news. Make arrangements to take all the valuable gifts and ask Duryodhana to go and bring back my loving Pandavas and their bride, with a royal honour, to Hastinapur." But Duryodhana was very depressed with the news and his father's loving attitude towards the Pandavas. He said to his father, "You seem to be very pleased with the news of the Pandavas' return. Don't you care about our future?"

Dhritarashtra replied, "I am not a child. I am aware

of the danger. I was pretending to be pleased in front of Vidura because he is among the Pandavas' well-wishers. So be very careful." Duryodhana said, "Then we must quickly do something, so that the Pandavas cannot claim Hastinapur." He suggested, "Let's attack Panchalas. After defeating them, we can make them captive. It will make them feel humiliated and not think of coming back."

Dhritarashtra appreciated his son's idea. But he could implement it only after a discussion with Bhishma, Guru Drona and Kripacharya. Bhishma objected to it and said, "Don't forget, Yudhishthira was crowned as the prince before going to Varanavata. So when he comes back, his kingdom should be given to him or otherwise divided into two halves."

Everyone in the court was satisfied with Bhishma's suggestion. Then Vidur left for Panchal, alongwith a number of servants, carrying expensive jewellery and gifts for the bride. Vidur received a grand welcome by the Panchal king. He said, "King Dhritarashtra of Hastinapur, Bhishma Pitamah, and all the people of Hastinapur are very glad with this marriage. They are very anxious to see the Pandavas with their bride, Draupadi, and Kunti." King Drupada told Vidura, "It is my good fortune that you have come to take Draupadi and Pandavas to Hastina-pur, but after the incident of Laksha-grih, I am afraid to sent them there.

Duryodhana, from time to time, has been planning to kill Pandavas. Will my daughter be safe there?"

Vidura became very thoughtful. He was unable to say anything because whatever King Drupada had said was true. Now when he was unable to answer, he looked towards Krishna for help.

Shri Krishna understood that Vidura needed help, so he said, "King! I believe and suggest that at least once, the Pandavas should go to Hastinapur, so that they could get back half of their kingdom."

King Drupada accepted Krishna's suggestion and gave permission to take leave, with lots of gifts, along with a number of maids for the daughter.

Pandavas, with wife Draupadi, mother Kunti, Vidura, and Krishna and Balrama reached Hastinapur. Bhishma, Guru Drona and Kripacharya greeted them. The people of Hastinapur were glad to see their princes once again.

Next day, when the Pandavas arrived at the court, King Dhritarashtra declared the division of Hastinapur kingdom between the Kauravas and the

Pandavas. King Dhritarashtra told Yudhishthira, "Son! I know that you are very intelligent, faithful and tolerant. There is no doubt that you are the legal heir of Hastinapur kingdom. Finding me as a ruler of Hastinapur for such a long time, my son Duryodhana has begun to assume himself as the next heir of this kingdom. That is why, all the elders in the family have decided to divide the kingdom between you and Duryodhana. I am sure you will happily accept this decision. I wish that you go to Khandprastha and form your kingdom there."

The people of Khandprastha were very excited to see their new king. They renamed the kingdom as "Indrapastha". Soon, its popularity spread to far-off lands.

Once Narada came to visit the Pandavas and said, "To avoid any misunderstanding between you brothers, you should spend your days turn by turn with Draupadi. Whoever breaks this law will be sent to exile for twelve years." The Pandavas agreed to this suggestion.

One night, some robbers stole away a Brahman's cattle. The Brahman went to Arjuna for help. As Arjuna left in a hurry, he forgot his bow and arrows in Draupadi's room. At that time, Yudhishthira was with her. He knew that if he went into the room, he would have to pay for it in the form of a twelve-year exile. But, in order to help the Brahman, he had to break the agreement. After bringing back the brahman's cattle, Arjuna went into exile. During the exile, he reached Haridwar.

ARJUNA MARRIES ALUPI

One day, when Arjuna dived into the river to take a bath, a beautiful damsel caught Arjuna's leg and pulled him towards her kingdom, situated under water. Arjuna asked her, "Who are you and why have you brought me here?"

The damsel replied, "I am Alupi, the daughter of Nagaraj. Now you are in the kingdom of Nagaraj, under the water. I want to marry you. You cannot leave the palace, unless you accept my proposal."

Arjuna had no other choice, so he married Alupi. Soon, a son was born to them. They named him 'Eravan'. Now, Arjuna decided to go back. So, Alupi brought her back to Haridwar. After returning back, Alupi gave Arjuna a boon, "All aquatic animals will consider you as a friend and whenever you come under water, you will become invisible."

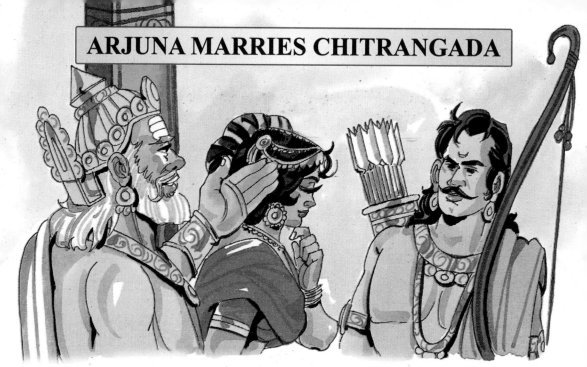

After leaving Haridwar, Arjuna reached Manipur. King Chitravahan welcomed him as his guest and made arrangements for him to stay in the palace.

One day Arjuna saw Chitrangada, the princess. He went to the king and said, "I have fallen in love with your daughter and would love to marry her." King Chitravahan said, "I will feel proud to get my daughter married to you if you promise me one thing. My grandson will be my heir after me, because I don't have any son."

Arjuna happily accepted this condition. Arjuna stayed in Manipur for three years. A son was born to Arjuna and Chitrangada. He was named "Babruvahan".

SALVATION OF THE FIVE

After leaving Manipur, Arjuna headed towards the south. He came across a hermitage, situated at a riverbank. Here, he came to know about the five holy lakes. Some Brahmans told him, "We are very scared because a number of fearsome crocodiles live in these lakes. Whoever goes to take a bath in these lakes, never returns back."

After listening to the Brahman, Arjuna fearlessly got into a lake. As soon as he entered the water, a crocodile swam towards him. Very swiftly, he caught its tail and pulled it out of the water. Just then the crocodile turned into a beautiful damsel. Arjuna was surprised to see this. He asked, "Hey Beauty! Who are you?"

She replied, "I am Varga, a dancing-girl from the court of Kuber. One day, when me and my four friends were going towards Nandanvan, we saw a hermit in deep meditation. We tried to disturb him. As soon as he opened his eyes, we smiled at him, but he cursed us, 'You have disturbed me, so you have to go to the earth and spend a hundred years as a crocodile.' We apologised to him, but he said, 'When an exceptionally bold warrior takes you out of the lake, you will get out of my curse and attain your real form.' " "Now, please help my friends as well to come in their real form," she requested.

Arjuna took mercy on the dancing-girls and helped them come out of the hermit's curse. The five of them thanked Arjuna and returned back to Nandanvan.

After visiting many holy places, Arjuna reached Dwarika. The king of Dwarika, Shri Krishna, had a sister named Subhadra. Balrama wanted her to marry Duryodhana, while Shri Krishna wanted her to marry Arjuna. One day, on Krishna's advice, Arjuna fled away with Subhadra in his chariot.

Subhadra's bodyguards could not stop Arjuna. So, they returned back and told Balrama about the abduction. He became furious at Arjuna and was about to go after him. Just then, he saw Krishna sitting very quietly. He exclaimed, "Kanha! In spite of your friend Arjuna's improper behaviour, you seem to be very calm!"

Shri Krishna replied, "Dear Brother! Be calm and think about it seriously. It is an honour that our sister will be the queen of Indraprastha. Arjuna is the most suitable groom for our sister." Balrama calmed down. Soon, Subhadra and Arjuna got married with great pomp and show and left for Pushkar.

After the end of the exile, Arjuna returned to Indraprastha. Both Arjuna and Subhadra received a grand welcome by the people of Indraprastha.

The people in Dwarika also came to know about the return of Arjuna from his exile. Shri Krishna and Balarama sent many gifts for the Pandavas. Mata Kunti and Draupadi arrived at Indraprastha. Months went by and soon, Subhadra gave birth to a baby boy. They named him Abhimanyu. From his childhood, he was as brave and strong as his father.

Once Narada appeared before Yudhishthira and said, "I met your late father in the heaven. At the time of his reign, he desired to perform a Rajsuya Yajna, but could not. Now, he wants you to fulfill his last desire."

Yudhishthira replied, "Munivar! I will surely fulfill my late father's wish." "That's good. But while performing the yajna, you have to be very careful because there are many people around who would try to disturb you," saying this, Narada vanished away.

After discussing the matter in his court, Yudhishthira sent an invitation to the kings of far-off kingdoms and also requested Hastinapur, Panchal and Dwarika kings to come.

On being invited, Shri Krishna reached Indraprastha. Everyone in Indraprastha was glad to see him.

Shri Krishna thought for a while and then said, "Hey Yudhishthira! Your idea of performing the Rajsuya Yajna is good, but before that you must kill Jarasandha. He is a very brave king. He has captivated many brave kings and princes. After hard ascetic practice, he has acquired many boons from Lord Shiva. I am his greatest enemy because I killed his son-in-law, Kansa, the king of Mathura. Shishupal, King of Chadi, the king Hans and Dimbakh are his supporters. With their co-operation and his arrogance, he has reached the peak of strength. That is why, he will never tolerate your idea of performing this yajna and will try to disturb the completion of your mission with all his might."

"So, how can we kill him?" asked Yudhishthira. Shri Krishna replied, "Rajan! you leave this on me. You only send Bhima and Arjuna with me. I will make Bhima kill Jarasandha. After his death, his supporters will not dare to face you." Then Shri Krishna told Yudhishthira, that Vrihadrath, his father, married two princesses of Kashi. But he had no children from them. A sage gave him a mango. Both the queens ate the mango and each gave birth to a half child. Being afraid, they threw away both the half babies. Jara, a giantess, saw the babies and tied them up with a piece of cloth. Both the sides got united and became a single child. The giantess took the baby to the royal court. The queens were shocked to see the baby, so they told the king the truth about the child. He named him Jarasandha. Just then a sage arrived and said, "Your son will only die when his body is torn apart and

thrown into opposite directions." Having known this, Bhima, Arjuna and Shri Krishna disguised themselves as Brahmans and left for Magadh. Soon, they reached mount Chaitak and attacked some Brahmans there. The Brahmans ran and told the whole incidence to King Jarasandha. The news was ominous for Jarasandha, so in order to protect his kingdom from any evil, he performed a huge yajna.

Then, the trio reached the place of yajna. Jarasandha bowed to the Brahmins and asked the reason for coming there. Shri Krishna replied, "Rajan! Today my friends have taken a vow of silence, so they will talk to you after midnight."

At midnight, Jarasandha came to meet them. He bowed to them very humbly and asked to introduce themselves.

Shri Krishna hid his identify, but while introducing Pandava brothers, challenged Jarasandha for a club fight with Bhima. Jarasandha burst out with anger after knowing the truth. He accepted the challenge. A fierce battle began between them. Bhima tore his legs from the middle into halves and threw them in opposite directions. Thus, Jarasandha died.

Then they met Sahdeva, Jarasandha's son. Shri Krishna made him the successor of the Magadh dynasty.

RAJSUYA YAJNA

After killing Jarasandh, Shri Krishna and the two Pandavas returned to Indraprastha.

Rajsuya was a grand yajna and it required a lot of wealth. So, Arjuna said to king Yudhishthra, "We must try to increase our state treasury as much as possible, so that there is no financial problem during the yajna."

Sage Vyasa agreed with Arjuna and instructed him, Bhima, Nakul and Sahdeva to go to the north, south, west and east directions respectively, and collect wealth by defeating different kings.

Soon, the Pandavas returned with huge wealth and the royal treasury was full with valuable stones, jewellery etc. Kings from far-off kingdoms, respective people and businessmen from the state, began to arrive in Indraprastha for the yajna. These invited guests brought valuable gifts for the Pandavas.

From Hastinapur, Bhishma, Guru Dronacharya, Kripacharya, Vidura and King Dritarashtra had come along with all the Kauravas. All the Kaurava brothers took over their respective responsibilities in the yajna.

Dusshasana took the responsibility of the kitchen. Guru Kripacharya was given the responsibility to wash the feet of the guests present in the yajna. Karna was given the work to give away alms. Sage Dhaumya was made the chief priest. The yajna was over without any obstruction and King Yudhishthira became an 'Emperor'.

SHISHUPAL

After the yajna, Emperor Yudhishthira addressed to all the kings present and said, "Please help me to choose the best king, so that we can conform the same respect to the other guests present in the yajna."

Sahdeva suggested Shri Krishna as the best person. However, some kings disagreed with Sahdeva's suggestion. Shishupal, the king of Chadi, was one of them.

Though Shishupal was Shri Krishna's cousin, because of Shri Krishna's popularity, achievement and his supernatural powers, he envied him. So, he could not tolerate Shri Krishna being conformed as the best king. So, he stood up and began to say derogatory words against Shri Krishna. Many other kings and princes, who were also against the Pandavas, like Duryodhana, supported Shishupal. It made Shishupal

become more outrageous. Listening to his meaningless words, Bhishma scolded him and asked him to sit quietly in his place. But, he began to say insulting words for him too.

When Shishupal's offensive behaviour crossed the limit, Shri Krishna rose from his place and said, "Shishupal! Enough is enough! I promised my aunt that I will tolerate only hundred of your guilts. Today, you have crossed that limit, so you need to be punished." But, Shishupal was adamant. Then, Shri Krishna chopped his head off from his Sudharshan Chakra.

Having Shri Krishna been crowned the best king, all other guests were given farewell with valuable gifts.

Everyone returned back to their kingdom, except Duryodhana and Shakuni. They were very impressed by Indraprastha, especially the royal court.

One day, both were going towards the court. On the way, Duryodhana assumed a lake to be a floor and he fell into it. Draupadi was looking at him through her window. She sneered at Duryodhana and said, "Son of a blind will always be a blind."

Listening to this, Duryodhana could not control his temper. He said to Shakuni, "How dare she call me blind?" Shakuni controlled him and said, "Don't worry, Draupadi will have to pay for this insult."

INVITATION TO PLAY DICE

Back in Hastinapur, Duryodhana and Shakuni were making evil plans to destroy the Pandavas and capture their beautiful city, Indraprastha.

Shakuni said, "Duryodhana! As you know, Yudhishthira is very fond of playing dice and nobody can defeat me in this game. So, let us organise a dice game and challenge Yudhishthira. In the game, I will throw the dice for you. And within a short time, we can win over all his properties and other valuable things. This will also give you an opportunity to take your revenge from Draupadi." Being pleased with Shakuni's suggestion, he sent Vidura to invite Yudhishthira for the game.

Though Vidura knew that it was a plan against the Pandavas, he had to obey his king's order. However, while inviting Yudhishthira, he also warned him

about Duryodhana's nasty plans. Next day, he left for Hastinapur with Draupadi and his brothers. They were given a warm welcome by Duryodhana. When Yudhishthira and his brothers entered the games-room, Shakuni was representing Duryodhana. Yudhishthira commented, "There should be honesty and no deceit at all in the game."

"The dice will prove it. If you are scared to play with us, you can withdraw. There is no commitment. First think and then begin to play the game," said Shakuni sarcastically.

"Mamaji! You are saying this because you know that I am very fond of this game. When anybody invites me for this game, I cannot resist myself, " Yudhishthira replied. Duryodhana said, "From my side, mama Shakuni will throw the dice. Do you accept it?" Yudhishthira accepted Duryodhana's conditions.

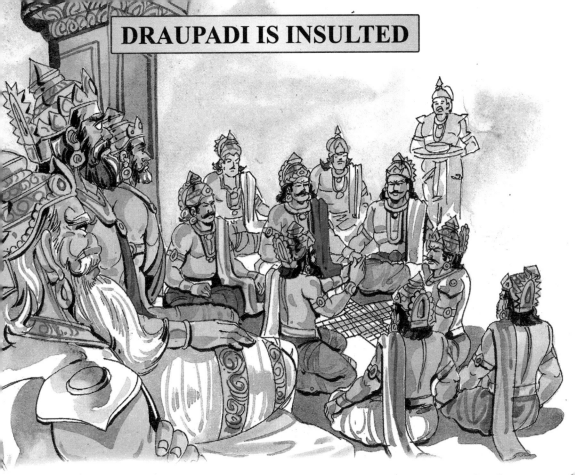

DRAUPADI IS INSULTED

The game began. Everyone was present to watch the game. Shakuni began to throw the dice and one after the other, he kept on winning the game.

Soon, Yudhishthira lost his kingdom, his maids and servants, his brothers and himself. Last of all, when nothing was left, he lost Draupadi in the game. Duryodhana had no end to his joy. In one blow, he won everything from the Pandavas. Very boldly he ordered Vidur, "Go and bring Draupadi. She will stay as a maid in my palace."

Vidura objected at Duryodhana's words and said,

"Duryodhana! Aren't you ashamed of saying such things. I will never do this disgraceful work. You are a fool! You are inviting troubles."

Vidur's words had no effect on him. He ordered his younger brother Dusshasana, "Go and bring Draupadi dragging."

Dusshasana obeyed his brother. He went to the guest-house and pulling Draupadi's hair, he dragged her into the games room. The Pandavas were sitting there helplessly in shame. Draupadi looked at them and said, "All of you should be ashamed of yourself to lose me, your wife, in the game." Then she turned to Bhishma, Dhritarashtra and others and said, "You all should also be ashamed of yourselves, watching me being insulted in such a way." Guru Drona, don't you see I am like your own daughter. What sort of Brahman and warriors are you? I want to ask you one

thing, when my husband lost himself in the bet, who allowed him to bet me in the game?"

There was complete silence in the games room. Everyone was helpless. Nobody answered her questions. Everyone hung his head in shame. Unfortunately, there was nobody, who could come forward and help the poor lady.

Karna also held a grudge against the Pandavas. He said to Dusshasana, "Take off all the royal garments from the Pandavas and also from Draupadi."

Dusshasana went forward and began to pull Draupadi's saree. Draupadi was helplessly staring at everyone in the room. But none came forward for her help. Then pitifully she recalled Shri Krishna. Shri Krishna could not resist a helpless lady's call. He

helped Draupadi keeping himself invisible. Dusshasana kept on pulling her saree and by the grace of Lord Krishna, Dusshasana became tired pulling the saree, but its length did not come to an end.

Suddenly a revelation in the air said, "Dusshasana! Stop yourself! You have crossed all your limits. Leave Draupadi alone otherwise, your end will come soon."

Dusshasana was so scared that he quickly left Draupadi's saree and sat far away from her.

Duryodhana went near Draupadi and said, "Even today, I cannot forget your words— 'Son of a blind will always be a blind,' so, come and sit on my left thigh." Bhima could not stand it anymore. He screamed aloud, "Duryodhana! I,

son of Pandu, take a vow in the presence of all, that one day I will break your thigh with my club. Dusshasana, I will tear your heart and with its blood, I will ask Draupadi to wash her hair."

Dhritarashtra was very sorry at his son's evil behaviour. He said, "Draupadi! You are the eldest daughter-in-law of my family. Therefore, you can ask me any three boons. I am very sorry at my son Duryodhana's bad behaviour. I agree that Yudhishthira has no right to bet you in the game after

losing himself, therefore, you are free. You are no
more a slave. Ask for you boons?"

Draupadi replied, "Respected father! I am the wife of
five brave warriors. So, I am obliged only two boons.
First, set king Yudhishthira free from slavery.
Secondly, return the Pandavas' princely clothes and
weapons." Draupadi's request was granted. Then
King Drithrastra asked Yudhishthira to go back to
Indraprastha and take over his kingdom as before. He
further asked him to forget about the game and
forgive Duryodhana for his misbehaviour. The
Pandavas bowed to Bhishma Pitamah and mother
Gandhari, and returned back to Indraprastha.

Duryodhana said to Dhritrashtra, "Father! Once again
you have done injustice with us. But, we will soon
take Indraprastha as our kingdom back."

PANDAVAS GO IN EXILE

In the course of time, Duryodhana once again made a spiteful plan and asked Pandavas for a game of dice.

Yudhishthira agreed as he wanted to take revenge from Duryodhana and get back his lost honour and dignity.

According to the conditions of the game now, the loser was to go in exile for 12 years and underground for one year. On being recognised while underground, he was to suffer the whole punishment again.

Listening to the conditions of the game, many of his friends and relatives advised Yudhishthira not to play the game, but he did not listen to anybody.

Once again a game of dice was played in Hastinapur. Shakuni threw the dice for Duryodhana and yet again, Yudhishthira lost the game.

Thus, the five brothers and Draupadi had to go in exile. They took off their royal costumes and put on simple clothes. Mother Kunti also wanted to go with her sons, but since she was ill, Vidur did not let her go. She decided to stay with Vidur. Then, the Pandavas bid farewell to everyone and left for the forest.

After the Pandavas had gone in exile, Narada came to King Dhritarashtra and said, "Hey King! I have come to say that you have done injustice with the Pandavas. One day, you will have to pay a heavy cost for it. After fourteen years, the whole of Kaurava dynasty will come to an end. And the Pandavas will rule again." When the royal priest, Dhaumya, came to know about the Pandavas' exile, he too followed them. Many other Brahmans and villagers also followed them. On reaching a forest, they built a hut to live in.

Yudhishthira said to Sage Dhaumya, "So many people have come with me in this forest. But, how will I feed them? Please help me, what should I do?"

Sage Dhaumya prayed for a few seconds and said, "Rajan! You should pray to Lord Surya. He is the father of all the vegetation and foodstuff in the world."

Lord Surya being impressed by Yudhishthira's meditation, appeared before him and said, "Son! I am impressed with your meditation. Say, what is your wish?" Yudhishthira said, "God! Give me a boon with which I can feed all my people who have come with me in this forest." Lord Surya gave Yudhishthira a pot and said, "Give this to Draupadi. Whenever she wants to cook food for her family and friends, she can acquire food from it. There will be no shortage of food, as long as you stay in the forest."

ARJUNA GETS CELESTIAL WEAPONS

When Sage Vyasa came to know about the Pandavas' exile, he advised them, "After the termination of your exile, there will be a fierce battle between you and the Kauravas. Hence, from now onwards start preparing yourself for it. Arjuna, you go to Mount Kailash and do hard ascetic practice to acquire the celestial weapons from Lord Shiva." Obeying him, Arjuna went off to the mount. Crossing many hindrances on the way, he reached Indrakul mountain. Here he met Lord Indra, who advised him to summon Lord Shiva through holy mantras.

All the Brahmans and people living in the heaven were terrified by Arjuna's hard ascetic practice. They went to Lord Shiva and said, "Dear God! A young man is performing a hard ascetic practice on mount Kailash. We are all scared. Please, quickly fulfill his desire." Lord Shiva said, "Don't worry. Today, I will do it."

He first decided to test Arjuna. He went there with

Parvati and dressed himself as a hunter. He sent a boar to attack Arjuna. Arjuna, quickly picked his bow and shot an arrow towards the animal. But before his arrow another arrow struck it. Arjuna became furious and screamed, "Who has dared to kill my prey?"

When Arjuna saw the hunter with a lady, he began to shoot arrows on him. Surprisingly, Arjuna's arrows returned halfway. Having been tired, he asked, "Hey glorious warrior! Who are you, with this lady?"

"I think you are still too immature to challenge anyone for a battle," the hunter said.

Arjuna did not like the taunting of a hunter and said, "Just let me finish my worship of Lord Shiva, then I will teach you a lesson." Saying this, Arjuna kept his bow and arrow aside and made a emblem of Lord Shiva out of ice. Then, he collected flowers to make a garland. He put the garland on the emblem and closed his eyes to began his ascetic practice.

When Arjuna opened his eyes, he saw that the garland that he had put on the emblem was coiled around the hunter's neck. Immediately, Arjuna understood that the hunter was none, but Lord Shiva himself.

Now, Arjuna bowed to him and said, "I have understood everything. The attack of the boar was your plan to test me. Have I passed your exam?" Lord Shiva was so impressed with Arjuna that he came to his real form and said, "Get up Arjuna! I am pleased with your ascetic practice. So, I grant you a boon of vision, which will enable you to win over all your enemies. Besides, I give you Pashupatastra."

After acquiring Pashupatastra, other gods like Varuna, Yama and Kuber also gave him many weapons and taught him how to use them.

Then, Arjuna went to Indralok to see Lord Indra. When the latter asked him the reason for his visit, Arjuna requested him to teach him the art of warfare.

After teaching the art of warfare, Lord Indra advised him to learn music and dance from Chitrasena.

Urvashi, a dancing-girl from the heaven, was highly influenced by Arjuna's bravery, so she began to love him. One night, when Arjuna was having rest, Urvashi entered his room. He was surprised to see her and said, "Respected mother! What has made you come here in these odd hours? You have not even informed before coming."

"A dancing-girl is nobody's mother or sister. I have

come here to win your love," replied Urvashi, looking at him lustfully. "You are very sacred for me because you are from my father-like Indra's court. Therefore, you are like my mother. Besides, once you have been my forefather Pururva's wife. So, in this way, you are a mother to all the Kauravas and Pandavas," said Arjuna.

Urvashi tried all her love tantrums on Arjuna, but in vain. At last, she burst out in anger and cursed Arjuna, "Like an impotent person, you have rejected my love, so for one year, you will have to remain like a eunuch."

Joining both his hands before Urvashi, Arjuna said, "Respected mother! Your curse is like a boon for me. I am very grateful to you." Urvashi was overwhelmed by Arjuna's self-respect, confidence and modesty. She gave him a boon that while living as a eunuch for a year, nobody will be able to recognise him.

BHIMA MEETS HANUMANA

It had been a long time since there have been any news of Arjuna. Everyone in the forest was worried about him.

One day Sage Lomash arrived at Kamyak, the place where the Pandavas were dwelling. Yudhishthira told him about his worries. The sage smiled and said, "I have met Arjuna at the Amaravati mountain. He has acquired all the celestial powers, along with Pashupatastra, from Lord Shiva. Besides, he has learnt the art of music and dance also from Chitrasena. Lord Indra has asked you not to worry about him and carry on your ascetic practice peacefully."

Everyone in the forest was relieved by this news. Yudhishthira now decided to go on a religious trip with his family. He invited Sage Lomash to come along with him to visit the holy places. After visiting many holy places, they reached

Badrikashram. He was so overwhelmed to see the natural beauty and peace in the atmosphere. So, he decided to stay there for few days.

One day, when Draupadi was sitting outside her hut, a beautiful

lotus flower dropped before her. She was surprised to see such a beautiful flower. She picked it up. She showed it to Bhima and said, "I want to give such beautiful flowers to your elder brother. But I don't think it is wise to give him only one flower. So please bring me some more flowers of this kind."

In order to fulfill Draupadi's desire, Bhima went towards the north-west direction, as the wind was blowing from that direction.

After walking a long distance, Bhima reached mount Gandhmardan. He was surprised to see the natural beauty over there. There were many

beautiful flowers blooming around, but the lotus flowers were to be seen nowhere. He saw a monkey lying on his way. When Bhima asked the monkey to move away from his way, he said, "I am old and sick, so I cannot move. If you need to pass by, move my tail a bit and go," said the monkey.

Bhima tried his best to move the tail,

but in vain. At last, Bhima folded his hands and said, "O, the high-spirited soul! I bow to you most humbly. Please show me your real form?"

When the monkey came to his actual form, Bhima was surprised to see that it was Lord Hanumana.

Hanumana said, "Both of us are the sons of wind. In this way, we are brothers. I will help you during the war against the Kauravas. Bhima bid him farewell and asked about the lotus flowers. Hanumana informed him that he would get the lotus in Kuber's garden. Thereafter, Bhima left for Kuber's garden. He was very pleased to see a pond full of lotus flowers there. But as he was about to pluck a flower, a number of guards warned

him to not to do so. Bhima said, "I have not come here to destroy your garden, but to collect some flowers for my elder brother. If you don't mind, please allow me take some. I will be very grateful to you."

The guards attacked him but it had no effect on Bhima. When they could not stop Bhima, they ran to their king Kuber and told him everything.

Kuber understood what Bhima wanted, so he asked his soldiers, "Make apology to Bhima and give him the lotus flowers." Bhima took the lotus and returned back to Kamyak forest. He gave the flowers to Draupadi, so that she could fulfill her desire.

Draupadi and the four brothers were very anxiously waiting for Arjuna. One day, they saw a celestial chariot coming down towards their hut in the forest.

The four Pandavas and Draupadi were overjoyed to see Arjuna after such a long time. First of all, Arjuna bowed to his elder brother Yudhishthira and Bhima. Then, he embraced his younger brothers Nakul and Sahdeva and greeted Draupadi.

Arjuna showed his brothers all the celestial weapons, which he had acquired from the different Gods in the heaven. As he was about to demonstrate their use, Narada warned him and said, "Arjuna! use them only when required. It will be a sin to use them without any purpose."

KING NAHUSH FREES FROM CURSE

One day, Bhima was strolling along in search of food. Suddenly a boa attacked and coiled around his body. Helplessly he asked, "Hey Serpent! May I know who you are and why have you trapped me like this?"

The boa replied, "I am your ancestor King Nahush.

Once I tried to taunt a Brahman, so Sage Agastya cursed me to become a serpent. By eating you, I will satisfy my hunger. If you want to save yourself, answer my questions correctly."

Bhima was stifling under the boa's grip, so he was unable to understand anything.

When Bhima did not turn up for a long time, Yudhishthira went out in search of him. When he found Bhima stifling under the boa's grip, he went close to them to answer all the questions correctly. In this way, Bhima and the boa, both were released from his curse. It made Nahush the celestial world.

DURYODHANA FEELS ASHAMED

The Pandavas were spending a tough time in the forest. Some Brahmans felt sorry for them and went to Hastinapur to tell King Dhritarashtra to help them.

Dhritarashtra felt unhappy, but Shakuni became happy. He went and told Duryodhana and Karna about it. Karna told Duryodhana, "Let's go and see their miserable condition ourselves."

Duryodhana agreed with him and left for Kamyak forest. He put up his tent in front of the Pandavas' hut and began to live there with pomp and show.

One day, Duryodhana and his friends planned to stroll along a nearby river. Coincidently, Gandharvaraj Chitrasena and his dancing-girls were taking bath in the same river then.

Duryodhana and his friends did not like this. So without thinking they attacked the Gandharvas. In return, Chitrasena shot his Sammohanastra. It made the Kauravas and party unconscious. In the meanwhile, Kauravas' ladies sent their slaves to Yudhishthira for help. When Bhima heard about the Kauravas' defeat, he said, "Very good! Duryodhana should also understand, how one feels to be a slave. When Chitrasena makes him work, he will loose all his pride." But Yudhishthira said, "Bhima! This kind of behaviour is not good. I agree that Duryodhana has always been mean and impolite towards us. But right now, it is a question of the Kauravas' dignity. So go and help Duryodhana and the royal ladies to come out from Chitrasena's captivity."

"Bhima and Arjuna went there and defeated Chitrasena. When Arjuna asked Chitrasena why he had captured them, Chitrasena replied, "Duryodhana was very pleased to know that you are spending a dreadful time in the forest and that is why, he is here. When Lord Indra came to know about his intention, he sent me here to teach him a lesson." Meanwhile, Yudhishthira arrived there. He said, "Gandharvaraj! I am grateful to you for not killing Duryodhana and his friends. Most humbly, I request you to please release them all." Chitrasena agreed and went off to the heaven. Yudhishthira said to Duryodhana, "My dear brother! Since you have come here, stay with us. But if you want to return back to Hastinapur, you go back happily. Give my respect to the elders." Duryodhana was ashamed of himself. So, he decided to return back.

One day Jaidrath saw Draupadi sitting all alone in her hut. He said, "Why are you spoiling your life in this jungle with the Pandavas. Come with me, I will make you my queen." Draupadi rebuked him in anger. But Jaidrath forcefully pulled her on his chariot. When Draupadi began to scream for help, the Pandavas immediately came for her rescue.

Finding the Pandavas in front, Jaidrath was afraid. He pushed Draupadi down from his chariot and rode away fast. But he was caught by the Pandavas.

Bhima tended to kill him, but Yudhishthira said, "No! He is our sister Dushala's husband. We cannot make her a widow." So with Draupadi's consent, Jaidrath was set free after shaving off his head.

YAKSHA EPISODE

After the Jaidrath incidence, the Pandavas left the Kamyak forest and reached Dwait forest. Here the Pandavas spent their time meditating and performing ascetic practice.

One day, a sage came to Yudhishthira and said, "Hey Rajan! I had only two holy sticks, hanging on a tree. When a deer rubbed his body against the tree, both the sticks fell on his horns. The deer ran away from there in fear. So please bring back my sticks because without sticks, I cannot perform the rituals."

The Pandavas took their bow and arrows and went off in search of the deer, but before they could do anything, the deer was out of sight. They tried their best to find the deer, but in vain. They were tired and thirsty. So they sat under a shady tree for rest.

Yudhishthira said to Nakul, "Climb on this tree and see if there is any source of water nearby."

Nakul climbed up the tree and saw that a little away from there, there was a lake. He got down from the tree and went off to bring water. When he came near the pond, he thought, "First let me quench my thirst, then I will take water for my brothers. As soon as he began to drink water with his hand, he heard a strange voice, "Wait! This is my lake. If you want to drink from it, you have to

answer these questions first." Nakul was very thirsty, so he did not bother to listen to the voice. As soon as he touched the water, he fell to the ground.

When Nakul did not return, Sahdeva went towards the lake to look for him. He became thoughtful to see his brother lying unconscious. He thought to quickly bring water from the lake and sprinkle it on his face. But as soon as he touched the water, he heard the same words, "Wait! First answer my questions, then touch the water. Otherwise, you will also face the same consequence as your brother did." Sahdeva too did not listen to the voice, so he also fell near the lake.

When Sahdeva too did not return, Bhima asked Arjuna to go. Arjuna was subsequently followed by

Bhima himself. But, he had to face the same consequences. At the end, Yudhishthira reached the lake looking for his brothers. He was surprised to see there his brothers lying unconscious. He thought to first quench his thirst and then find the person, who had put his brothers in this condition.

He went near the lake and as he was about to touch the water, he heard, "This is my lake. If you want to drink its water, first answer my questions. If you pretend not to hear my words, you will also face the same consequences as your four brothers did." Yudhishthira said, "I think my brothers have neglected your warning and now are undergoing its result. You are the owner of this lake. Ask your questions. I will try to answer them. After satisfying you, I will drink water."

Yaksha asked many questions to Yudhishthira and having been satisfied with his answers, he offered to give life to only one of his brothers. Yudhishthira replied politely, "Lord! Out of mother Kunti's three sons, I am alive. But Mata Maadri's both sons are lying unconscious. I would request you to please grant life to either Nakula or Sahdeva."

Overwhelmed by Yudhishthira's greatness, Yaksha came back to his real Yamaraj form and said, "I am impressed with your intelligence and kind-heartedness. So, I am making all your four brothers come alive."

With this, the four Pandavas were alive. Then Yamaraj asked Yudhishthira to ask him for two boons. Yudhishthira said, "Lord! I have promised a

Brahman to bring him the sticks which were trapped in a deer's horn. Please grant me a boon through which I can fulfill my promise and help that Brahman. In my second boon, I want that nobody could recognise us during the period when we are underground." After listening to Yudhisthira's wishes, Yamaraj said, "Rajan! That deer was nobody but me and here are the sticks and be underground in Viratanagara." Saying this, he disappeared. On his advice, the Pandavas moved towards Viratanagara. They buried their weapons under a big tree.

After this, Yudhishthira disguised himself as a Brahman named Kanak and went to king Virata. The king was impressed by his knowledge and intelligence. So, he appointed Yudhishthira as his legal advisor.

Since Bhima was very fond of eating, he took the work of a cook in the royal palace of Viratanagara and was called Vallabh. Nakula named himself as Granthik and began to work in the royal stable, while Sahadeva named himself Tantipal and became a shepherd.

Likewise, Draupadi became a maid in the palace. She named herself as Sairandhi. Arjuna opted to teach music and dance to princess Uttara and her friends. He named himself as Brihannala. Thus, the five Pandavas began to live there hiding their real identify.

One day Keechak, queen Sudeshna's brother came to the palace to meet her. He saw Draupadi and was fascinated by her beauty.

In a quiet place, he said to her, "The moment I saw you, I fell in love. If you agree to stay with me, I will keep you like a queen."

It made Draupadi become wild with temper. She said, "You rogue! You don't know me. Five brave Gandharvas protect me. If they come to know about your bad intentions, they will kill you."

Being rejected by Draupadi, Keechak asked her sister to send Draupadi to his residence by any means. Sudeshna knew that her brother's persistence was useless, but she was helpless to obey him as he was taking care of the management of her kingdom.

So, one day, using an excuse Sudeshna sent Draupadi

to Keechak's house. When Keechak cunningly tried to grasp her, she pushed him hard and fled from there. But soon, Keechak seized and kicked her several times openly in the court, but there was no one, who would come for her rescue. Draupadi felt humiliated. She went to Bhima and told him everything.

Bhima became furious. He, at once, got ready to kill Keechak. But Draupadi warned him not to do anything that might reveal their identity.

Bhima became quiet and began to think of a plan. He told her, "Draupadi! Try to be a little humble and draw his attention towards yourself. And when he begins to have faith in you, ask him to meet you at night in the music room."

After this Draupadi became humble towards
Keechak. This increased his courage and one day
he desired to meet her alone, in quiet. Draupadi
said, "I respect your words, but five brave men
guard me throughout the day. To meet me, be in the
music room at midnight." That night, Keechak
went drunk to the music room. Bhima was already
there dressed like a woman. Keechak thought her to
be Draupadi and opened his arms wide to embrace
her. Bhima swiftly crushed him to death with his legs.

DRAUPADI REASSURES THE QUEEN

Next morning, the news about K e e c h a k ' s death spread like forest fire in the whole kingdom. His sudden death was a suspense for everyone.

On being asked by the queen, Draupadi replied, "I had already told you, that five invisible Gandharvas are my bodyguards. I had also warned your brother. But, he did not listen to me and lost his life." Listening to her, Sudeshna felt offended and said, "Your bodyguards can harm us also. Hence, leave me alone and look for another job for yourself."

Draupadi said, "Queen! You are a very generous lady, you gave me shelter, so how can I harm a person, who had helped me in times of need. Just let me stay here for thirteen days more. And I assure you that my stay here will be a boon for you."

KAURAVAS INVADE VIRATANAGARA

No sooner the Pandava's began living underground, Duryodhana sent his detectives to different states to spy against them. He wanted to trace them by all means, so that he could send them in exile again.

One day, when he got the news about Keechak's death, he became restless, because one such power had saved Draupadi in the games room earlier.

So, Duryodhana decided to attack Viratanagara for two reasons. First, since Keechak was dead, the Viratanagara kingdom had become very weak. He could easily defeat King Virata. Secondly, if the Pandavas were hiding in Viratanagara, he could find them out to be sent in exile again.

So Duryodhana, Karna and King Shusharma invaded Virata-

nagara. With the sudden invasion, King Virata became fearful. When Yudhishthira as Kanak saw this, he consoled the king and said, "Rajan! Please

don't worry. Just send your soldiers with me. I will not allow the Kauravas to enter your kingdom."

Yudhishthira had a fierce battle with the Kauravas, but none could recognise him. At the end of the day, Shusharma cunningly captured King Virata. When Yudhishthira came to know about this, he asked Bhima to go and get him released.

So with a huge Virata army, Bhima followed Shusharma. Under Bhima's guidance, the soldiers fought fiercely in the battlefield. They surrounded Shusharma and broke his chariot. When Bhima caught him and was about to kill him, Yudhishthira said, "Don't kill him, give him a stiff warning that he should never try to invade this state again, otherwise, its result will not be good."

ARJUNA REACHES THE BATTLEFIELD

After a treacherous defeat of the Kauravas, Karna attacked Virat Nagar again. This time, he captured their sixty thousand cows. Though prince, Uttar was a brave warrior, but since his charioteer was killed in the war, he was unable to go to the battlefield.

When Arjuna came to know about the prince's problem, he sent a message to him through Draupadi. She told the prince that his sister's music teacher Brihannala had once worked as Arjuna's charioteer, so appoint him your charioteer.

Prince agreed and thus Arjuna, as a charioteer, reached the battlefield. But, looking at Karna's huge army, prince Uttar became nervous and asked Arjuna to retreat. Arjuna said, "Prince! We have to drive away our enemies from our boundary. It is not wise for a Kshatriya to run away from the

battlefield. If you cannot face the enemies. Come to my place and let me fight for you."

Having being allowed, Arjuna came down from his chariot and took out his weapons from the ground. He also took out his favourite bow and arrows, along with some celestial weapons.

Then, he rode towards the battlefield and flinged like a storm at his enemies. The Kauravas' soldiers could not face Arjuna's attack.

Having recognised his beloved student, Guru Dronacharya went to Bhishma and said, "No doubt, this is Arjuna, disguised as a eunuch."

When Karna came to know about it, he was very excited. When he informed it to Duryodhana, he

was also excited. Then Bhishma interrupted them and said, "Prince! You are mistaken. The period of exile has ended. Now you have to decide whether you want a war or peace." Duryodhana replied, "I will not return Indraprastha to the Pandavas at any cost. Hence, let us start preparing ourselves for a big war."

"OK, you take half of your army and safely drive away the sixty thousand cows to Hastinapur, while we—Dronacharya, Karna, Ashwatthama and myself, will try to stop Arjuna," said Bhishma. Duryodhana obeyed him and went towards Hastinapur.

When Arjuna realised the absence of Duryodhana from the battlefield, he understood the matter. So, he also moved towards Hastinapur. When Karna, saw Arjuna coming, he tried to stop him. But he could not stand against Arjuna's arrows.

Arjuna used his Sammohastra and surrounded Duryodhana to take back all the cows from him.

ABHIMANYU MARRIES UTTARA

After the war, Arjuna buried all his weapons again. When King Virata heard about the victory, he had no end to his happiness. He asked Kanak to play chess with him. While playing the game, he said, "Look, my brave son defeated the Kauravas so easily."

Kanak replied, very politely, "The victory was definite because of Brihannala." King Virata became outrageous at his answer. He threw the chess-board on his face and said, "Brahman! How dare you compare my son with a eunuch? Do you want to say that my son is not brave." As the chess-board hit upon Kanak's face, it started bleeding. Just then, Prince Uttar came in the room. He was surprised to

see Yudhishthira's face bleeding and asked the matter.

The king said, "Son! I have done this crime because he was comparing you with a eunuch."

When prince Uttar told his father the truth about Yudhishthira and the other Pandavas, the king apologized and said, "I am grateful to all of you. I want to get married my daughter Uttara to Arjuna."

Yudhishthira replied, "Rajan! As you know, Arjuna has taught music to Uttara. So for a guru, his pupil is always like a daughter. Hence, I would like Uttara to marry Arjuna's son Abhimanyu." King Virata happily accepted the proposal. Everyone in and around the state of Viratanagara was invited in the wedding ceremony. Shri Krishna, Balarama, the Panchala king Drupada and his son Dhristadyumna also came to attend it.

After the ceremony, a grand meeting was called to discuss about the further plan relating to the completion of their thirteen years of exile.

King Virata, King Drupada, Dhristadyumna, Shri Krishna, Balarama and the king of Kashi were all present at the meeting.

Sanjay, the royal priest of Panchala, reached Hastinapur and said to Dhritarashtra, "Maharaj! Since the Pandavas have completed their thirteen years of exile and being underground, please return them their kingdom. If Duryodhana plays his tricks again, he will pay for it severely. As you know, the Pandavas are unconquerable. So, it is impossible for the Kauravas to win over them." Dhritarashtra thought deeply upon Sanjay's statement.

When the peace treaty was laid before the court, Duryodhana refused to accept it. He said, "Without war, they will not get back their kingdom."

Bhishma tried to make him understand and said, "Duryodhana! It is better to return their kingdom peacefully. Otherwise, the Pandavas' victory over the Kauravas in the coming battle is definite." Duryodhana said, "Please don't worry. Although the Pandavas are unconquerable, we have great warriors like Pitamah, Guru Drona, Guru Kripacharya and Karna. It is not that easy to defeat us."

Dhritarashtra was confused. After a while, he said, "Sanjay! I am unable to decide anything. My son is insane, therefore, he is not listening to anyone. I am afraid that all those who will fight against the Pandavas will have to face defeat." With the Kauravas' decision, Sanjay returned back.

When back home, Sanjay told the Pandavas what the Kauravas desired. Pandavas were shocked to know that they wanted war. In fact, the Pandavas never wanted bloodshed. They were trying their best for some other peaceful solution. Instead of half the kingdom, the Yudhishthira asked for only five villages. But Duryodhana denied even that.

Yudhishthira was very unhappy at his cousin, who was constantly putting a threat of war, while the Pandavas were trying to avoid it.

So, they went to Shri Krishna for help.

Shri Krishna consoled Yudhishthira and said, "Dear brother! Please don't get so depressed. I know that according to the conditions made in the games-room, you have completed 13 years of exile and being under-ground, but foolish Duryo-dhana is denying his own words. He is lost in his pride, that is why, he is unable to understand any-

thing. But if you want, I may go there as an envoy of peace."

When Shri Krishna was about to leave for Hastinapur, Draupadi said, "Keshava! I have not washed or tied my hair for the last 13 years because I had taken a vow to wash it with Duryodhana's blood. But since all of you have decided not to fight the Kauravas, I will go to my father and ask him to take revenge for my insult."

Shri Krishna said, "Draupadi! Don't worry. This is a must because I know Duryodhana will not agree for peace. I am going there with an aim that in future, people do not blame the Pandavas. Everyone should know that though the Pandavas were on the right path, they had to face injustice and tried their best to stop the war."

King Dhritarashtra believed that Shri Krishna was

able to make Duryodhana understand. But Duryodhana had a different plan. He said, "Why not we captivate Krishna, because without him the Pandavas will be helpless and we will get the whole kingdom without war." Everyone in the royal court was very shocked to hear Duryodhana's statement. After arriving in Hastinapur, Shri Krishna first went to Vidur's house to meet his aunt Kunti. Kunti asked about her sons and her daughter-in-law. Shri Krishna said, "Dear aunt! As you know, your sons are unconquerable. They will defeat the Kauravas and take revenge of Draupadi's insult, and take back the kingdom of Hastinapur."

After this, he met Duryodhana who invited Krishna for dinner. Shri Krishna said, "Duryodhana! Since I am an envoy, only after finishing my mission, I will have food with you. So right now, I cannot accept

your invitation." When Vidur told Shri Krishna about Duryodhana's plans, he said, "Duryodhana's idea of making me a captive is impossible."

Early next morning, Shri Krishna reached the royal court with Vidur. After giving them the message of the Pandavas, he said, "Maharaj! Pandavas do not want to go for a war because it will lead to bloodshed. Yudhishthira has requested Duryodhana to do justice to his younger brothers. You are like a father to the Pandavas, so please give them back their kingdom, so that they can live there peacefully." King Dhritarashtra said helplessly, "Krishna! I also want the same, but Duryodhana is adamant to his words. What to do?"

Then Shri Krishna said, "Duryodhana! you should respect your father's feelings and return Indraprastha to the Pandavas." Bhishma and Dronacharya supported

him, but in vain. Gandhari also tried to make Duryodhana understand, but in vain. When Duryodhana tried to make Krishna captive, he took out his Sudarshanchakra and took a gigantic form.

Then he warned Duryodhana, "You are not only selfish and arrogant, but also addicted to wicked

nature. That is why you are planning to make me captive. You are not aware of my strength. If I want, within minutes, I can ruin the Kaurava dynasty and make the Panadavas the ruler of Hastinapur." He left the royal court in anger and went to meet Kunti. Bidding her farewell, he got on his chariot and headed towards Karna's hut.

Luckily, Karna was alone in his hut. Krishna said to him, "Karna! By now you must be aware of the truth that you are Kunti's son. Kunti, in her unmarried state, begot you with Lord Surya's boon. Thus, you are Pandavas' brother. And being the eldest among the Pandavas, you an eligible heir for the royal throne. So, come with me and support your brothers."

KUNTI MEETS KARNA

Karna listened to Shri Krishna with great patience. He said, "I know that Kunti is my real mother, but she floated me in the river to die. If my God mother would not have accepted me, I would have died. How can I disregard my God mother who has always helped me? Duryodhana always gives me respect, while the Pandavas have always disregarded me. He considers me as the main contestant against Arjuna. I cannot be disloyal to Duryodhana. So, please forgive me and ask me for some other favour."

Shri Krishna was very disappointed at Karna's statement, as it was his last effort. Then, Vidur went and asked Kunti to go and talk to Karna. He feared that since Karna envied Arjuna, with the help of his father's boon, he would easily defeat Arjuna.

Early next morning, Karna found Kunti in front of him. He wished her and asked, "Maharani! Say, how can I help you?"

Kunti replied, "Son! Call me mother instead of Maharani, because I gave birth to you. You are the eldest among the Pandavas, hence, leave the support of the Kauravas. I have committed a sin by disregarding you at your birth. But then, I was unmarried and being scared of the society, I took that cruel step. Now join your brothers. It will be a repentance for my sin. Besides, with your support, my sons will surely defeat the Kauravas and get back their lost kingdom."

After listening to Kunti, Karna said, "I know everything about my birth. All these years, I was craving to hear the word 'son' from your mouth. Didn't your heart melt when people called me the son of a charioteer?"

Kunti replied, "You don't know the agony I faced

after disregarding you. Whenever people called you a charioteer's son, I felt offended. But when I came to know that both my sons are going to fight against each other in the war, I cannot keep myself aloof."

Karna replied, "Dear mother! I cannot leave Duryodhana because I have spent my childhood in his guidance. Besides, he has always helped and supported me as his friend. So now, when it is my turn to pay back, how can I turn my back to him?"

Kunti lost all hope after listening to Karna's statement. Karna, too, was not feeling good to dishearten his mother. Hence he said, "Mother! I promise you that I will not kill either of Yudhishthira, Bhima, Nakul and Sahdeva, but Arjuna

has always been my rival. So, our battle will be a conclusive one. But whatever will be the result, you will still be a mother of five pandavas." After this, Kunti embraced Karna and returned back.

After the failure of the peace negotiation with the Kauravas, Yudhishthira said, "Now we have no other choice, so let's prepare ourselves for the war."

The Pandavas divided their army into seven units and each unit was headed by King Drupad, Chekitan, Dhristadyumna, Bhima, Virat, Satyaki and Shikhandi.

Since Bhishma was bound with his promise to safeguard the kingdom of Hastinapur, he had to lead the Kaurava army against the Pandavas.

So, he laid two conditions before Duryodhana, "First, although I am bound to fight from your

side, I will not kill the Pandavas. But, I assure you that I will not allow their army to stand before me. Secondly, Karna will not enter the battlefield. Though he is among your well-wishers, he does not have any respect for me." After thinking a lot, Duryodhana accepted Bhishma's conditions.

Now, both the sides began their preparations for the great war. They were trying to add more and more soldiers in order to establish a huge and powerful army.

During those days, Dwarika, under the kingship of Shri Krishna, also had a very huge and powerful army. Since Shri Krishna had a very close relationship with the Pandavas, everyone was sure that he will give his support to the Pandavas. In spite of it, some of Duryodhana's supporters asked Duryodhana to go and meet Shri Krishna.

MEETING WITH SHRI KRISHNA

Since Duryodhana was aware of Shri Krishna's huge army,

without any delay, he reached Dwarika. As Shri Krishna was sleeping, Duryodhana sat near his head. Meanwhile, Arjuna too arrived there for his blessings. Finding him sleeping, he sat near his legs.

After some time, when Shri Krishna woke, he was surprised to see Arjuna and Duryodhana in his room. Both expressed their desire to have Shri Krishna and his armies' support in the coming war. Shri Krishna felt hesitant for a while and said, Today, let me tell you a thing clearly that at one end, I have my huge 'Narayani Army' and at the other end, it is me, all alone taking part in the war.

"Though I know that Duryodhana came first to meet me, but as I saw Arjuna first, I give him the

advantage to decide first."

Arjuna replied, "Madhusudan! I don't need your vast army. I only need your support. It will be a boon for me." Duryodhana, on the other hand, was smiling at Arjuna's foolishness. He quickly said, "Krishna, Give me your army. With its help I can easily conquer the Pandavas." Then both left for their respective kingdoms.

King Shalya of Madra was a brother of Maadri, the wife of king Pandu. When he heard of this war, he took his huge army and marched towards the Pandavas to support them.

When Duryodhana came to know this, he planned a crooked trick. He made special arrangements to welcome King Shalya in his route.

King Shalya was greatly impressed by these arrangements. But when he came to know the truth, he was shocked. Although he was impressed by Duryodhana, but still, he had a fixed intention to

help Yudhishthira. Pertaining to the situation, he said, "Duryo-dhana! I and my army are very impressed by your hospitality on the way. Therefore, we thank you for the same. Say, what can I do for you?"

Duryodhana replied, "I would like you to fight from my side." King Shalya was shocked at Duryodhana's wicked request.

Without answering, he left the place and went to Yudhishthira to tell everything. Since Yudhishthira was known to act justly, he advised the king to help Duryodhana. As he was his debtor, it was his duty to repay his debt at any cost.

King Shalya bowed to the king for his generosity and said, "Though I will fight in support of the Kauravas, I will not kill any of the Pandavas."

Then, the Pandavas ordered their army to march towards Kurukshetra, the battlefield.

RULES OF THE GREAT WAR

Having reached Kurukshetra, the Pandavas pitched their tents. At night, they sat together to decide their warfare strategy. The Kauravas made their camps just opposite the Pandavas'.

When Yudhisthira saw this, he, after consulting Shri Krishna and his brothers, declared to begin the war. Encouraging his soldiers, he said, "Give all your strength to this war, because the chief commander of the Kauravas' army is Bhishma Pitamah."

Then, both the armies stood opposite each to their commanders. Shri Krishna was Arjuna's charioteer.

Everyone in the battlefield was strictly asked to abide by certain rules, which were:

1. A day of war will end with the sunset.

2. The war will be fought with full justice.

3. An unarmed person will not be attacked.

4. A person, who has accepted defeat, will not be attacked again.

5. A person who is involved in the work of carrying away of armaments, food, medicines and other important things required in the war, should not be attacked.

6. Nobody will attack a tent, where the injured ones are being treated.

Bhishma encouraged his soldiers and said, "As long as you live, keep on fighting. No matter whatever terrible situation you come across, don't show your back or retreat." This encouraging statement of Bhishma increased the morale of his army.

Arjuna was supposed to fight against Bhishma in the war. Hence, Shri Krishna took Arjuna's chariot to where he was standing. Arjuna looked at Guru Drona, Kripacharya, Aswatthama and others around. 'I have to fight against these great men and well-wishers,' thinking this, he was deeply moved. He thought, 'To attain victory in the war, how can I raise my weapon against the men who have brought me up? It is sinful for me, even to think of such an ugly thing. I don't want victory over the dead bodies of my relatives. I cannot do this at any cost.'

Thinking about the dreadful results of the war, Arjuna let down his bow and arrows.

Shri Krishna was surprised to see Arjuna so depressed. So, in order to bring him out from his depression, he tried to preach him on a religious performance. In the due course, the collection of such teachings came to be known as "Bhagwat Geeta."

Shri Krishna said to Arjuna, "You are grieving in vain. Our soul is immortal, so nobody can destroy it. One has to die one day and then take birth again. This is part and parcel of our life circle. Hence, forget about this perishable body and do your duty forgetting its results."

In order to clear his doubts, Arjuna asked him several questions. Shri Krishna replied to them all, as his friend and a philosopher.

Then Arjuna asked, "Dear friend! You are giving importance to duty. What is it? And why is it so important?" Shri Krishna answered, "Every human being has a duty to perform and it is his right. Its fate depends upon a person's duty. As you sow, so you reap. Remember, only God is liable to give you a fruitful result. You are a Kshatriya, hence it is your duty to fight for justice. In a war, there can be only two results—one is to become either victorious or be killed while fighting. So, don't think about the

result of the war. A person performing his duty, without any attachment to worldly life, is a karmayogi. Take out all your

feelings from your soul." Shri Krishna also tried to explain Arjuna about the four yogas based upon the true knowledge, religion, power and duty. After listening to his teachings, Arjunas was relieved from his agony. He asked him, "Hey Devaki Nandan, please show me your actual celestial appearance?" With this, Shri Krishna gave Arjuna a celestial sight.

YUDHISHTHIRA TAKES BLESSINGS

As the war was about to begin, there was a sudden commotion in the Pandavas' troop. King Yudhishthira, had taken off all his weapons and walked towards the Kauravas' troops. Everyone in both the troops was surprised. He went straight to Bhishma, touched his feet and said, "Pitamah! Duryodhana has forced us to go for this war, so please give us your blessings."

Bhishma was impressed at Yudhishthira's modesty. He said, "Son! Be victorious. My best wishes are always with you." Similarly, he went to Guru Dronacharya, Kripacharya and his maternal uncle Shalya, and took their blessings.

Thereafter, he came back to his army and the great war began.

BEGINNING OF THE GREAT WAR

The war between the Kauravas and the Pandavas began. Dusshasana was leading the Kaurava army, while Bhima was leading the Pandava side.

Abhimanyu, Arjuna's son, was facing Bhishma, the Kauravas commander-in-chief. Very boldly, he was showering his arrows towards them. Looking at Abhimanyu's courage, a part of Kauravas' army surrounded him, but he was not afraid. He kept on fighting bravely, showering his arrows towards his enemies. Just then, a group of the Pandava army saw Abhimanyu surrounded by enemies. They quickly came forward for his rescue.

At the other end, Prince Uttar was fighting against King Shalya. He killed the king's charioteer and the horses. It made King Shalya's spur into action. He threw his spear at Prince Uttar. It pierced through the prince's chest, killing him on the spot.

When Prince Shwet, Uttar's elder brother saw his brother dead, he fiercely attacked the Kauravas. After killing hundreds of Kauravas soldiers, he also lost his life. So, on the first day of the war, the Kaurava army, under the leadership of Bhishma, was at the upper hand. A number of Pandava soldiers were slain and wounded. On the other hand, the Kuaravas were very excited about it.

THE SECOND DAY

On the next day, the Pandavas decided to follow a new strategy of warfare. It was to encourage their soldiers to fight bravely against Kauravas.

Arjuna and Dhristadyumna then planned a new strategy called Vajravyuh (a military array). As planned, Shri Krishna took Arjuna's chariot right in front of Bhishma. Finding Arjuna facing him, Bhishma welcomed him by showering his arrows at him. Arjuna, too, welcomed him in the same way. Then, a fierce battle began between the two great warriors of that time. Whenever Bhishma sent his arrows towards Arjuna, he would return them midway back to the Kauravas. At the other end, Duryodhana came to save his soldiers from Bhima's disasterous attack. The competition between the two club warriors continued, but Duryodhana could not

stand for long against Bhima's attack and soon fainted. It made his charioteer quickly ride out of the battlefield.

On the other side, a never-ending battle was going on between Bhisma and Arjuna. Just then, Satyaki killed Bhishma's charioteer. The unbridled horses ran away, with Bhishma, from the battlefield.

At the third end, Dhristadyumna was facing Guru Dronacharya. Both the warriors were old rivals. Dronacharya broke Dhristadyumna's chariot. It led to a fierce battle between Bhima and Guru Drona. At the sunset, the battle for the second day came to an end.

THE THIRD DAY

On the third day, Bhishma, once again, reorganised his army. This time, he gave the command to Duryodhana. On the opposite side, Arjuna and Bhima were commanding the Pandava army.

Just then, Shakuni entered the battlefield with his soldiers. But, very soon, Abhimanyu drove him away.

From the very beginning, Bhima had been dominant over Duryodhana. While fighting, Bhima struck hard on Duryodhana with his club. It made him faint. So, his charioteer had to take him away.

Arjuna remembered his vow to kill Bhishma, Guru Drona and Karna. So, he took his chariot near Bhishma. Getting close to Bhishma, Arjuna became more aggressive. And a huge battle continued for a long time, but there was no result. So, Shri Krishna took out a wheel from his chariot and threw it towards Bhishma, like a Sudharshanchakra. But Arjuna intruded and stopped the chakra midway because it was against the rule of the war. Besides, Shri Krishna had already vowed not to pick up a weapon in the war.

On the fourth day, Bhishma once again reorganised his army and flung at the Pandavas. Duryodhana took a sly step. He, along with his soldiers, surrounded Abhimanyu, but luckily, Dhristadyumna saw this and soon came there with his army. Then, a fierce battle was fought between them.

When the battle ended with the sunset, Duryodhana asked Bhishma, "Pitamah! Why is it that the Pandavas' condition in the battle is improving day-by-day?"

Bhishma replied, "This is because they are on the path of righteousness. Duryodhana, there is still time, go and make peace with the Pandavas and stop the forthcoming disaster."

THE FIFTH DAY

On the fifth day, Guru Drona and Arjuna were facing each other. Whatever weapon Guru Drona sent towards Arjuna, Arjuna would destroy it halfway. When Duryodhana saw it, he began to shout at Guru Drona thinking that he was deliberately trying to make himself feeble before Arjuna. Guru Drona could no longer stand his verbal assault.

Therefore, he scolded him and said, "Duryodhana! We are trying our best to defeat the Pandavas. But, you still don't have any knowledge about their celestial energies. That is why, you are behaving like this." Duryodhana then sent Bhurishrawa, an expert swordsman to fight against Satyaki. Satyaki was very badly injured in this encounter.

On the sixth day, Guru Drona killed his opponent's charioteer, and then broke the chariot. Then, he flung over the Pandava army like a disaster. The Pandava, too, did not show their back and the war became more fierce. On the other end, Duryodhana got very badly injured, while encountering Bhima. So, with Kripacharya's advice, he left the battlefield.

After the sunset, Duryodhana went to Bhishma to know about the present condition of the war. Bhishma condoled him and said, "Duryodhana! Stop suspecting the fidelity of your soldiers. All are fighting faithfully on your behalf. There is either victory or defeat in a war."

THE SEVENTH DAY

As per the new strategies for the seventh day, it was planned that Bhishma would fight against Arjuna, Dronacharya would fight with Virat, Bhima would face Duryodhana and his brothers, and Nakul and Sahdeva would fight against Shalya.

Guru Drona defeated Virat and killed his son Shankh. On the other end, Ashwatthama made Shikhandi lose his courage. Yudhishthira, while fighting Shrutayu, killed his charioteer. Shrutayu fled for his life from the battlefield. Chekitan, Kripa-charya and Dhristaketu encountered Bhurishrava. Nakul and Sahdeva injured Shalya. By the sunset, both the armies retreated to their camps.

THE EIGHTH DAY

Once again, Bhishma stood in the battlefield with a new strategy. In the early hours of the day, Bhima killed Duryodhana's eight brothers, while on another end, Arjuna's son (born out of Alupi), Eravan, was killed by a giant named Alambush. When Ghatotkachh, Bhima's son, saw this, he began to roar awfully and flung at the Kauravas killing hundreds of them. The rest of the soldiers began to run away in terror.

Ghatotkachh then threw his weapon, "Shakti", aiming Duryodhana. But, it lost his aim and killed his elephant.

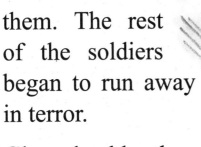

Guru Drona came for Duryodhana's help. Since it was dusk and the war ceased for the day, Duryodhana was very unhappy. He told his brother, Dusshasana, "We must make sure that Shikhandi never comes in front of Bhishma, otherwise, he will stop fighting because fighting with a eunuch is against his rules."

THE NINTH DAY

On the ninth day, Abhimanyu was fighting against the demon Alambush very bravely, while Ashwatthama was having dominance over Satyaki. Arjuna bravely faced Guru Drona.

At the other end, Bhishma was showering his arrows over the Pandava soldiers. Just then, Arjuna broke Bhishma's bow with his arrows.

But, Bhishma did not move. He picked up another bow and began to shower his arrows towards Arjuna and the Pandava army.

To stop Bhishma, Shri Krishna took his Chakra and began to move towards him. Then Bhishma, said, "What a luck! I will be killed by the master of the universe." But, Arjuna stopped Shri Krishna from doing so, by making him remember his vow.

At night, all the Pandava chiefs met to discuss how to win over Bhishma. When nothing turned up, they went to Pitamah himself. Bhishma told the steps, through which they can stop him. After saluting him, the Pandavas returned back to their camps.

Arjuna attacked Bhishma, with Shikhandi in front. Soon, he showered his arrows on Bhishma, but Bhishma did not move from his place. He was bound with his vow to not to attack an eunuch. Soon, his whole body was pierced with Arjuna's arrows. He fell on his back upon the arrows, as if he was lying on a bed. There was complete silence in the battlefield. Forgetting about war, everyone gathered around Bhishma. Shri Krishna and Arjuna also went close to him.

Although his whole body was pierced with arrows, there was a smile on his face. Arjuna shot three more arrows just under Pitamah's head, as if it was a head-rest for him.

He called Arjuna near him and said, "Son! I am very thirsty." Now Arjuna shot another arrow on the ground near his head. Soon there spurted a spring of water. It reached Bhishma's mouth. Thus, he quenched his thirst.

With Bhishma on the death-bed, it was the beginning of the Kauravas' downfall.

Though Bhishma was lying on a bed of arrows, he looked normal. Actually, he had got a boon of death at will from his father. He still praised Arjuna's archery and blessed him. Then, he called Duryodhana closer

to him and said, "There is still time. Stop this war and do justice with Pandavas, and return back their territory. This is my last warning and if still you don't listen, believe me, the end of the Kaurava dynasty is near."

Bhishma's warning had no effect on Duryodhana and he quickly left the place with his army.

When Karna came to know about Bhishma, he apologised to him for his bad behaviour.

Bhishma very lovingly said, "Karna! I know that you are not only a Kshatriya, but also the eldest Pandava. I have always been displeased with you, because you have been supporting Duryodhana for his wrong doings. Now stop supporting Duryodhana and go to your brothers."

Karna said, "Pitamah! I know that the Pandavas are my brothers. But Duryodhana has always given me great respect. Hence, I cannot betray him." Bhishma understood that Karna was determined to his decision.

In the Kaurava's tent, a meeting was going on as to who should be the next commander of their army. Duryodhana wanted to make Karna the new commander, but Karna very politely refused the proposal and said," I think Guru Drona is most suitable for this." So, Guru Drona was declared the commander-in-chief.

Kaurava army believed that under the commander-ship of Guru Drona, they will easily defeat the Pandavas.

Karna had once taken a vow that he would never fight along with Guru Drona. So, as soon as Guru Drona took the command, Karna began to move away from the battlefield. But, Guru Drona knew that the only person, who would take the place of Bhishma is Karna, so, his presence in the war was necessary. Hence, he said, "As Kaurava army is passing through a terrible situation, your presence in the army is more important. Therefore, forget all your past rivalries and fight along with me for the sake of Kaurava's victory." Karna accepted Guru Drona's advice.

THE ELEVENTH DAY

Although Guru Drona was fighting in favour of Duryodhana, he was very fond of the Pandavas, especially Arjuna. So, he was trying to avoid Arjuna in the battlefield. When Karna and Duryodhana saw this, they persuaded him to capture Yudhishthira. Drona agreed and rode towards Yudhishthira.

But luckily, the Pandavas came to know about Duryodhana's stupid plan. So, the security for Yudhishthira was increased.

When Drona entered the battlefield, Dhristadyumna was ready to face him. At another end, Sahdeva with Shakuni, and Nakul with Shalya, were ready to exchange blows. Abhimanyu, Satyaki and Virat were also very fearful. Abhimanyu fearlessly

fought bravely with Kritvarma, Jaidrath and Shalya.

At another site, Bhima was destroying the Kaurava army with his club. When Shalya fainted after receiving a severe blow from Bhima's club, there was commotion among the Kauravas.

When Guru Drona saw Yudhishthira, he rode towards him. Yudhishthira was alert, he tried his best to stop him. But then there was a loud outcry among the Pandavas, "Save King Yudhishthira, otherwise, Guru Drona will capture him." As soon as Arjuna heard this, very swiftly, he appeared before Guru Drona and began to shower his arrows towards him. Helplessly, Guru Drona had to retreat.

Guru Dronacharya was very upset as he had failed to capture Yudhishthira. So he said to Duryodhana, "It is impossible to capture Yudhishthira when Arjuna is around. So, somehow try to take Arjuna away from his elder brother."

When Shusharma heard this, he promised to take Arjuna away from Yudhishthira, with help of his brothers. So, in the battle, he challenged Arjuna for a war. Arjuna could not reject a Kshatriya's challenge, so he went after Shusharma.

Once Arjuna was gone, Guru Drona rode towards Yudhishthira. But under tough security and presence of Dhristadyumna, Satyaki, Nakul, Drupad, Virat and Bhima, he was once again unable to capture Yudhishthira. Duryodhana and Karna reached there with a hundred elephants in

Dronacharya's support and set them free to trample down Bhima. But Bhima turned them back stamping their own soldiers.

After this, Duryodhana sent Bhagdatta, with a huge elephant, to attack Bhima. The elephant picked Bhima with his trunk and dropped him hard on the ground. Everyone assumed Bhima to be dead. But soon, Bhima got up and injured Bhagdatta and his elephant with his huge club. As a result, they began to run away from the battlefield. When Arjuna,

encountering with Shusharma, came to know about Bhima being attacked by Bhagdatta, he became worried. He asked Shree Krishna to take the chariot towards Bhima. Shusharma and his soldiers began to follow Arjuna. Shusharma attacked Shree Krishna and Arjuna with two of his celestial weapons. But Arjuna destroyed them with his arrows, and then with another arrow, he stopped Shusharma and his army from moving forward.

Then, Shree Krishna turned Arjuna's chariot towards the place where Bhagdatta was fighting with Bhima. They found Bhagdatta and his elephant on the way and killed them.

Twelve days were gone, but still, there was no sign of a result. The Kauravas had been facing defeat from time to time. Many soldiers and brave warriors were killed in the war. Guru Dronacharya was still unable to capture Yudhishthira. It made Duryodhana lose his temper and shout at the guru. Dronacharya felt offended, but very politely replied, "Duryodhana! Don't get so impatient. You know that it is impossible to capture Yudhishthira in Arjuna's presence. But I promise you that today, I will capture him."

Shusharma once again challenged Arjuna for war. Arjuna, accepting the challenge, followed him. Then Dhristadyumna, Satyaki, Kuntibhoj, Virat and Bhima safeguarded Yudhishthira. Guru Dronacharya suddenly attacked them, but was unable to reach Yudhishthira.

The war strategy made by Guru Drona for that day was very powerful. Only Arjuna could reply to that, but he was not there. Everyone in the Pandavas' camp was worried about how to break the Chakravyuh. At the end, Abhimanyu said, "I know how to go inside the Chakravyuh. But I don't know how to get out from it." Bhima said, "OK, You break the Chakravyuh and enter into it. After that, we will also enter it for your rescue."

With this, Abhimanyu ordered his charioteer, Saumitra, to move towards Dronacharya. But his charioteer said, "Prince! Do not enter the Chakravyuh. It can be very dangerous for you."

Abhimanyu did not listen to him. When he was swiftly running toward Guru Drona, Duryodhana

173

came in between, with a huge army. But Abhimanyu
killed thousands of his soldiers. When Guru Drona
realised that his soldiers were not able to stop
Abhimanyu, he took Ashwatthama, Karna, Shakuni,
Jaidrath, Ashmak and Shalya with him and
surrounded Abhimanyu. He still did not get vexed
and fought bravely with his enemies.

None could not stop Abhimanyu. He was moving
forward like a storm and soon, he entered Drona's
Chakravyuh. Jaidrath closed the entry. So, Bhima
and other Pandavas remained outside it.

Though Abhimanyu was alone in the Chakravyuh,
he bravely fought and killed Duryodhana's son,
Laxmana.

Laxmana's death made Duryodhana more arrogant.

He ordered his soldiers, "Kill Abhimanyu as soon
as possible, otherwise, he will alone destroy the
whole Kaurava army." With this order, Karna with
his soldiers attacked Abhimanyu from the back.
This was, of course, against the rules of the war.

Being attacked from the back, Abhimanyu armour
quivered and his bow and arrow broke. But, he was
not afraid. He picked up the broken wheel of his
chariot and killed dozens of soldiers.

Dusshasana's son attacked him with his club, but
Abhimanyu cleverly snatched the weapon from him

and no sooner had he replied to the attack, he received a hard blow on his head and the great warrior died.

Thereafter, Arjuna got the news about his son's death and how the Kauravas had attacked him from the back. Bhima also told him about Jaidrath and how he closed the Chakravyuh, and therefore, he could not go in for his help. Arjuna was very angry at Jaidrath. He made a vow to kill Jaidrath before sunset, otherwise, he would commit suicide.

THE FOURTEENTH DAY

When Jaidrath came to know about Arjuna's vow, he wanted to return back to his kingdom. But Duryodhana promised to give him full guard.

On the fourteenth day of the war, Arjuna first destroyed the army led by Duryodhana's brother, Dusshasana. Then, he rode his chariot close to where Dronacharya was standing and said, "Guruwar! Kindly tell me where he is. After killing him, I will settle with those, who have killed my unarmed son. I know you are one of them."

Guru Drona was ashamed, because he was also a part of that shameful crime.

He said, "Arjuna! I am here for Jaidrath's security, so, without defeating me, you cannot reach him."

Listening to this, Arjuna took his bow and tended to shoot an arrow. Just then, Shree Krishna stopped him and made him remember his vow. After a long search, he found Jaidrath surrounded by hundreds of guards. When Duryodhana saw Arjuna, he ran fearfully to Dronacharya and said, "Guruvar! Kindly do something. Jaidrath's life is in danger." Guru Drona then gave Duryodhana an armour to put on and face Arjuna. He had planned that as long as Arjuna was away from Yudhishthira, it was easier for him to capture the latter.

At another end, when Satyaki was tired of fighting, Dhristadyumna asked him to take rest. As Satyaki was leaving the battlefield, they heard the sound of the conch of Krishna. Yudhishthira became thoughtful regarding Arjuna's safety and requested Satyaki to go with his army for Arjuna's help.

"Arjuna has entrusted me with the responsibility to

guard you. Therefore, how can I go from here? As long as Arjuna's safety is concerned, don't worry, Shri Krishna is with him," he replied.

Yudhishthira was still worried. Though he himself was a great warrior, but the death of Abhimanyu had made him possessive towards Arjuna. Considering the mental state of Yudhishthira, Satyaki gave his responsibility to Bhima and went off for Arjuna's help. After a few hours, when there was still no news from Arjuna, he sent Bhima too.

On the other side, Arjuna was ferociously breaking all the barriers to reach Jaidrath. Just then, Shree Krishna saw Duryodhana coming towards them very swiftly. He told Arjuna to kill Duryodhana first, as he was responsible for this terrible outbreak.

Arjuna shot an arrow towards Duryodhana, thereby destroying the chariot and the horses. He left Jaidrath there and fled for his life.

At another side, a huge battle was being fought between Dhristadyumna and Guru Drona. At one stage, he reached Guru Drona's chariot and was about to kill him. Dronacharya not only stopped him, but also attacked him. With great difficulty, Dhristadyumna managed to save his life.

Then, he shot his arrows of fire towards Satyaki, but he nullified them. Dronacharya was getting weary. Suddenly, he saw Bhima coming towards him. He was unable to stop him. He was now sure

that Jaidrath will not live for long.

In the last phase of the fourteenth day, Bhima fought with Karna, Satyaki with Bhurishrava and Arjuna with Jaidrath. Duryodhana was very fearful, when he saw the ferocious look of the Pandavas.

Bhima was trying to reach Arjuna, while the Kaurava army was trying to prevent him from doing so. Just then, Karna emerged in front of Bhima with his soldiers. A fierce battle began between the two. Karna was trying to stop Bhima with his arrows. Inspite of being injured, Bhima kept on moving. He broke Karna's chariot and killed his horses.

It angered Karna and he flung at Bhima like an hungry lion. Bhima was not ready to accept defeat.

With his club, he made a hard blow at Karna and broke his bow. Then he pulled him down from his chariot. When Duryodhana saw Karna in distress, he sent his younger brother Durjay for his help. But Bhima killed him. After this, Durmukh and Duryodhana's other brothers came, but Bhima killed them all. Karna too, fled for his life.

After this, Duryodhana sent Vikarna and seven of his brothers to fight against Bhima, but soon, they were also killed. Bhima was now tired and wanted to retreat back to his camp, but Karna once again attacked him. A fierce battle began between them. Karna broke his bow and then his sword. Bhima

was now unarmed. Karna was about to kill him, just then, he remembered his promise made to Kunti. When Krishna saw the unarmed Bhima encountering with Karna, he asked Arjuna to help him.

Arjuna was outrageous in anger. He showered his arrows at Karna and he, once again, fled from the battlefield. Just then, he saw Satyaki fighting with Bhurishrava. He became thoughtful, because he had appointed him to protect Yudhishthira.

A terrible war was on between them. They fought first with their swords and then with clubs.

Arjuna was still looking for Jaidrath. Just then, he saw Bhurishrava, who was going to kill Satyaki with

his sword. So, he chopped off Bhurishrawa's right arm. It gave Satyaki a chance to kill him with his sword.

The fourteenth day was close to end, but Arjuna was yet to complete his promise of killing Jaidrath.

The sun was about to set and Arjuna was still in search of Jaidrath. Everyone was becoming restless. Just then, there was a solar eclipse. Jaidrath came out from his guards' protection and rejoiced. In a few minutes, the sun began to shine again. Shree Krishna told Arjuna, "Parth! This is the right occasion to keep your promise."

Arjuna shot an arrow towards Jaidrath. Soon, his head was separated from the body and fell on his father's lap, who was praying for his son's long life.

After Jaidrath's death, there was joy and excitement in the Pandava camps. The Kaurava army was so excited that they were not ready to stop fighting, in spite of the sunset. Ghatotkachh destroyed thousands of Kaurava soldiers. Duryodhana sent Karna to face this disastrous demon.

Karna was unable to stop him from destruction. Now, he had only one weapon, Amoghshatra, left that he had saved to kill Arjuna. But, he had to use it against him. It made Ghatotkachh feel powerless. So, he fainted and died.

DEATH OF GURU DRONA

Everyone was discussing how to kill Guru Drona. King Yudhishthira said, "A sorrowful message to Guru Drona can make him stop fighting."

Shree Krishna found the idea reasonable and ordered, "Spread the news that Ashwatthama is dead. This news will make him leave his weapons. Just then, Dhristadyumna will kill him."

At first, the Pandavas criticized this plan. But when Shree Krishna gave them an example of killing of Bali by Lord Rama, everyone agreed. Bhima killed an elephant named Ashwatthama and shouted, "I have killed Ashwatthama. Ashwatthama is dead." When Dronacharya heard this, he became very sad.

He wanted to clarify this news. He knew that Yudhishthira would never tell a lie, hence, he asked Yudhishthira about the truth.

Yudhishthira said, "Yes, Ashwatthama is killed but it was not your son, but an elephant." As soon as Yudhishthira completed half of his sentence, Shri Krishna asked to play drums aloud. So, Dronacharya was unable to hear the last part of his answer. Hearing the news, Dronacharya threw away his weapons on the ground and began to mourn over his son's death. Just then, Dhristadyumna killed him.

THE FIFTEENTH DAY

Karna and Arjuna were facing each other. Bhima came there with his huge army for Arjuna's help. When Duryodhana saw this, he sent his brother, Dusshasana, with a huge army to help Karna. No sooner had Bhima seen Dusshasana, his anger reached its extreme. He began to visualize the games-room scene, when Dusshasana dragged Draupadi over there, from her bedroom.

Thinking about the incidence, Bhima flung at Dusshasana like a dreadful demon. He cut off his right arm and killed him. He then filled a bowl with

his blood for Draupadi to wash her hair. After Dussharana's death, Duryodhana was feeling very unhappy and helpless.

Finding him unhappy, Ashwatthama said, "Duryodhana! Now the Pandavas are blazing violently in their retaliation. It is wise to compromise with them, otherwise, the Kauravas' end is sure." But, Duryodhana was a very wicked person. He did not like the truth from Ashwatthama. Immediately, he called another troop of army to attack the Pandavas.

At the other side, an awful battle was going on between Arjuna and Karna. Karna suddenly shot his 'Agniban' towards Arjuna, Shree Krishna quickly

rode the chariot towards the lower part of the ground, hence, Karna missed his aim.

The arrow passed through Arjuna's crown. Karna was annoyed and angry. Suddenly he said, "Arjuna! Please wait for a while. My chariot's wheels have got stuck into the mud and therefore, it is not moving forward. Hence, don't attack me.Otherwise it will not be just."

Shree Krishna said, "Karna! Words like fair-unfair, just and unjust, do not suit you. Was stripping off Panchali's clothes in public justified, or planning to burn the Pandavas alive fair, and killing young Abhimanyu unarmed fair? And was kidnapping

Draupadi from the ashram justified? Now, when your life is in danger, you are talking about justice before Arjuna." Karna tried his best to take out the wheels of his chariot from the mud, but he did not succeed. So, he decided to fight from the ground.

Shri Krishna said, "Arjuna! Kill this wicked man at once. He is a shame for all brave warriors. He is the one who misled you away from the battlefield, and as a result, your son was killed." Encouraged by him, Arjuna cut off Karna's head with his arrows.

KRIPACHARYA'S ADVICE

Duryodhana was extremely upset to know about Karna's death. With a heavy heart, he headed towards the camps to seek Kripa-charya's advice. Karpacharya said, "Duryo-dhana! You have lost all your near and dear ones in the war. Every-one tried his best to help you in all possible ways, but no one could succeed. You failed everywhere because you were never on the path of justice, whereas the Pandavas never left the path of justice. There is still time, make peace with Yudhishthira. He is very modest and truthful."

But Duryodhana said, "Now since I have lost all my near and dear ones in the war, how can I live in peace?"

Shalya was appointed the new commander-in-chief of the Kaurava army.

King Yudhishthira came forward to fight with him. First, they fought with their bow and arrows, then they started fencing. Shalya lost his life in the encounter.

After his death, Duryodhana sent his another brother to fight against the Pandavas. But, brave Bhima killed them all. Thereafter, Bhima challenged Duryodhana for a war. He wanted to kill him as soon as possible, and break his right thigh to keep his vow.

On the other side, a fierce battle was going on between Nakul and Shakuni. Shakuni, as usual, was playing his cunning tantrums over Nakul to defeat

him. Just then Sahdeva said, "Wicked person! You have committed many abominable sins. You have led to this blood shed. So, get ready to die."

Saying this, Sahadeva slayed Shakuni with his arrow.

After Shakuni's execution, Duryodhana was all alone. Nobody was alive to support him. He was looking very tired and depressed. Now, he was receiving the statements of Vidur, Bhishma and Guru Drona. Everyone tried to make him understand, but in vain. Then he said to himself, 'I must suffer for the sins I have done.'

GANDHARI'S SAFETY MEASURES

Gandhari was much thoughtful about his son Duryodhana, who was left all alone to fight the Pandavas. She called him and said, "Son! With the strength of my chastity, I can protect you. Hence, go and take bath in the holy river and come in front of me nude. By removing the strip from my eyes, I will give you a supernatural power. It will cover your whole body with impenetrable armours that will have no effect of Bhima's attack on you." Duryodhana accepted his mother's statement. But, when Duryodhana was going nude to his mother after taking bath, Shri Krishna stopped him and said, "Duryodhana! Aren't you ashamed of going naked in front of your mother? At least, cover the lower part of your waist with something." Duryodhana, obeying him, covered the lower part of his waist with some banana leaves. But when Gandhari removed the

strip from her eyes and looked at Duryodhana with her supernatural power, his whole body turned into an impenetrable armour, except the thigh area, which was covered by leaves.

Gandhari scolded him and said, "Duryodhana! What did you do? I asked you to come naked." Duryodhana told her that he had done so at Shri Krishna's advice. Gandhari was very depressed.

Duryodhana was so scared of Bhima that he hid himself in a lake. When the Pandavas came to

know about it, they challenged him for a war.

But Duryodhana did not come out. So, the Pandavas decided to go into the water. When Duryodhana saw the Pandavas coming, he came out and agreed to fight. First Bhima came forward with his club. A club fight began between the two and it continued for a long time. When Duryodhana looked tired, Shri Krishna tried to make Bhima remember his promise. Bhima then gave a hard blow, with his club, on Duryodhana's right thigh. Duryodhana fell on the ground and then Bhima kicked his head.

Now Bhima's both the vows were kept. When Duryodhana was lying on the ground with his broken thigh, Balarama came there.

Balarama was very angry when he heard that Bhima had broken Duryodhana's thigh. He scolded Bhima in anger, "Stupid! Don't you know that attacking below the waist is against the rules of war."

Bhima kept quiet, but Shri Krishna came forward and said, "Brother! Bhima would never have done this if Duryodhana had not insulted Draupadi in public and asked her to sit on his right thigh. This insult made Bhima to take a vow that one day, he would brake the thigh on which Duryodhana desired to make Druapadi sit. Today, he has kept his vow."

He continued, "Dear brother! Aren't you fond of your nephew Abhimanyu? This Duryodhana executed him, when he was without any arms. Besides, his friend Karna attacked him from the back. Have you also forgotten the kidnapping of Draupadi by Jaidrath? So, there is no harm in going against the rule for these wicked people. He never thought about his limits, just-unjust, true-untrue, etc."

Balarama became calm after hearing this criticism. But Duryodhana said, "The Pandavas were not ready to leave the path of righteousness, neither they were ready to take any wrong step. But you encouraged them to do wrong. Now, I will die like a brave warrior to reach the heaven, but the Pandavas will face the hardship of life."

THE SEVENTEENTH DAY

When Ashwatthama came to know that Bhima had broken Duryodhana's right thigh, he was very sad. He did not forget how the Pandavas had killed his father, Dronacharya. His heart was blazing to take revenge with the Pandavas. He said to Duryodhana, "Prince! I cannot see you in this helpless condition. I promise you that tonight I will slay all Pandavas."

Duryodhana was impressed by Ashwatthama's speech. He made him the commander of the Kauravas for the eighteenth day. He said, "Friend! I have utter faith in you that you will surely keep your promise. Then only, my soul will rest in peace."

At midnight, when everyone in the Pandavas' camp was sleeping, Ashwatthama decided to meet Kripacharya. He told him his plan. Kripacharya

opposed to his plan and scolded him. "You should be ashamed of this stupid plan. By doing so, you will increase you father's sins, as he killed Abhimanyu, when he was unarmed."

Kripacharya's words had no effect on Ashwatthama. He was adamant on his decision. So, Kripacharya followed him to the Pandavas' camp. First, they killed Dhristadyumna and his soldiers. Then, they went to where Draupadi's five sons were fast asleep. Assuming them to be the Pandavas, Ashwatthama killed Draupadi's sons.

Then, they slayed all the Pandava soldiers and burnt all their camps. Then, he went to Duryodhana who was anxiously waiting for him.

Duryodhana was very glad to hear his deeds. He said, "Friend! The work which you have done for me today, Pitamah or even Karna were not able to do." Saying this, he left his soul in peace.

On the eighteenth morning, when the Pandavas came to know that Ashwatthama had killed Draupadi's sons, along with the entire Pandava army, they had no end to their grievance. Only eight Pandavas were alive now — five brothers; mother Kunti; Draupadi; and Uttara, Abhimanyu's widow. Draupadi's grievance was intolerable. She screamed aloud at the Pandavas and said, "Don't anyone among you have the courage to take revenge of your sons' executor, Ashwatthama."

The Pandavas condoled her and said, "Draupadi! Be calm. We are also very sad at our sons' death. We will pull him out from within the earth."

Pandavas reached Sage Vyasa's hermitage. Ashwatthama was hiding here. He was scared to find the Pandavas standing close to him. Then, he very swiftly picked a strand of grass and threw it towards the Pandavas saying, "Go and fall at a place where the seed of a young Pandava is growing." As soon as Ashwatthama completed his sentence, the straw turned into a sword and went to Uttara, Abhimanyu's pregnant widow. Shri Krishna destroyed this sword and thus, saved the unborn child.

Then, Bhima pulled Ashwatthama out of the hermitage. A fierce battle was fought between them. At the end, Ashwatthama had to accept defeat. There was a precious stone on Ashwatthama's forehead. Bhima presented it to Draupadi.

END OF THE WAR

With the death of Ashwatthama, the great war of Mahabharata came to an end. The eighteen day long battle left no sign of the Kauravas, while the Pandavas were victorious.

After winning the war, the Pandavas returned back to Hastinapur. Dhritarashtra, with great affection, embraced the four Pandavas—Yudhishthira, Arjuna, Nakul and Sahdeva. But he had hatred for Bhima because he had killed his favourite son, Duryodhana. Shri Krishna presented an iron statue of Bhima before him. Assuming it to be Bhima, he embraced it so tightly in his arms that it broke. Dhritarashtra thought that he had killed Bhima and he began to cry aloud. Then, Shri Krishna told him the truth and condoled him.

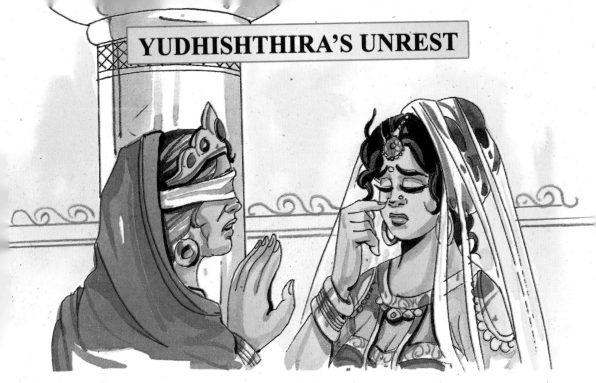

Gandhari was lost in grief at her sons' death. The Pandavas also showed their grief towards their brothers' death. Gandhari, held Shakuni, Karna and Dusshasana responsible for this great destruction. She also consoled Draupadi at her sons' death.

Then, they went on the bank of Ganga and performed the last rites of all their dead ones.

Yudhishthira now became the king of Hastinapur. But, he was not happy because he got the kingdom at the cost of the death of his near and dear ones. He was even unable to lead a normal life. So, he decided to abandon the worldly life and become a sage. Draupadi and his brothers tried their best to make him change his decision, but in vain.

But, Sage Vyasa made Yudhishthira agree to accept the crown. So, a grand preparation began for the coronation.

Yudhishthira went to take Bhishma's blessings. Bhishma was anxiously waiting for the sun to reach the north, so that he could abandon this world and reach the heavenly abode. He gave Yudhishthira many important instructions regarding his duty as a king. As the sun reached its northern horizon, Bhishma deserted the world. His last rites were performed with great honour.

After the death of Bhishma, Yudhishthira was once again lost in grief. But, Dhritarashtra said, "It is not wise for a Kshatriya to be so irresolute. Hence, control yourself and rule over Hastinapur happily."

KRISHNA MEETS A SAINT

After the Pandavas got settled in their kingdom, Shri Krishna bade farewell to them and left for Dwarika.

On his way back home, he met a saint, Utank. He asked him about the Kauravas and the Pandavas. Shri Krishna told him everything. After listening to him, he became impatient and held Shri Krishna responsible for the whole disaster. Shri Krishna showed him his real celestial form and told him to ask for a boon. The saint said, "God! Whenever I am thirsty, I may acquire water immediately." Granting him the boon, he headed for Dwarika.

After some time, the saint desired to drink water. Suddenly, a low-caste man appeared there, with a leather waterbag. The saint looked at him in anger. The man disappeared, and Shri Krishna appeared instead. He said that the man was nobody but Lord Indra himself, with nectar. The saint felt very sorry for losing such a grand opportunity.

DEATH OF SHRI KRISHNA

Once a few Brahmans came to Dwarika. The prince decided to examine their supernatural power. He disguised himself as a pregnant woman and asked them, "If you are a divine personage, tell whether the baby inside my womb is a boy or a girl?"

The Brahmans became angry at it and cursed him, "Wicked Prince! You have mistrusted our caliber. Hence, we curse you that you will be the cause of downfall of the Yadava dynasty."

The Brahmans' curse proved to be true. The Yadava dynasty came to an end. Balarama could not withstand this shock and soon passed away. One day, while Shri Krishna was lying under a shady tree, he became a hunter's prey and died.

PANDAVAS GO TO THE HEAVEN

Yudhishthira performed an Ashwamedh Yajna and became an emperor. He ruled over Hastinapur very skillfully. Dhritarashtra and Gandhari received full honour. Kunti and Draupadi took great care of them.

When King Dhritarashtra and Gandhari became old, they decided to become hermits. Kunti, too, desired to go with them. So, the trio bade farewell to the Pandavas and left for a forest.

Unfortunately, one day a fire broke out in that forest and Dhritarashtra, Gandhari and Kunti were burnt to death. The sudden death of his parents, downfall of the Yadavas, and death

of Balarama and Shri Krishna made King Yudhishthira very mournful. He, too, decided to leave the worldly life. So, he entrusted the responsibility of Hastinapur to Prince Parikshit, the grandson of Arjuna, and left for a pilgrimage with Draupadi and his brothers.

Passing through the mounta

in peaks, they reached Himadri. But, except Yudhishthira, nobody could cross the glacial path and they fell down from there, one after the other, and died. Yudhishthira was quite unhappy at their death, but he did not stop his journey. He continued with his pilgrimage. A dog was following him from the beginning. In fact, it was Yamraj himself.

Suddenly, Lord Indra appeared before him. When Yudhishthira payed his respect to him, he blessed him and said, "Your four brothers and Draupadi have already reached the heaven after death. I have come to take you with me, on my chariot."

So, King Yudhishthira went and sat on the chariot. The dog also sat on the chariot, but Lord Indra objected it. Hereupon, Yudhishthira said, "God! This dog has crossed the dangerous glacial path of the Himadri, which my brother and Draupadi failed to cross, and they lost their lives. If there is no place for him in the heaven, I will also not go."

After saying this, Yudhishthira came down from the chariot and began to walk on foot. Lord Indra tried to give him many excuses, but in vain.

Looking at this, Yamraj came to his original form

and blessed him. After this, Yudhishthira got on the chariot with Lord Indra and reached the heaven.

In the heaven, Yudhishthira was surprised to see Duryodhana being treated in a princely manner. He said, "Is this the heaven? If yes, why is this wicked Duryodhana here? Where are my friends, brothers, Draupadi and others? I cannot stay here."

Lord Indra just called a pathfinder and asked him to take Yudhishthira to his wife and brothers.

The path, through which they passed, was covered with human bones, flesh, blood, etc. and it was smelling dreadfully. Yudhishthira was worried

about his family. He asked the pathfinder, "How far is my family?"

The pathfinder replied, "If you don't want to walk further, let us go back." Yudhishthira was feeling unrest due the terrible smell, so, he decided to walk back. But, as soon as he turned his back, he heard some heart rendering voices, "Don't leave us behind. Have mercy on us and stay here. Your presence has made us feel relieved for a while."

Yudhishthira's heart melted after hearing their painful voice. He said to the pathfinder, "If my stay here brings relief to these people, I must stay here."

Yudhishthira then heard many voices together and now he could recognise them. They were his brothers' and Draupadi's voices. He was very upset and angry. He said to the pathfinder, "You go back. I will stay with my family."

Just then the whole atmosphere around him became very pleasant and bright. And the Almighty God said, "Son! I have been testifying you from time to time. And each time, you proved to be better."

Yudhishthira asked, "May I know, why have you been testifying my potentiality from time to time?"

The Almighty God replied, "Yudhishthira! You have been a very honourable and a justice-loving ruler. One who justifies the happiness and sorrow of his people, can be justifiable to his people."

He went on, "Son! None of your brothers, wife and mother is in hell. These are all an image prototype facsimile of your near and dear ones. We are now in the heaven." Yudhishthira was very delighted to hear this and he voluntarily accepted death.

THE GIST OF GEETA

- Why do you worry? Nobody can kill you. The soul neither takes birth, nor does it die.

- It has always been the best; it is all for the best and it all will always be for the best. Never repent on the past, nor even worry about your future. Learn to live in the present only.

- Which loss makes you sad? What had you brought with you and what have you lost? Whatever you had is lost now. What you have here is lost here. Whatever you got was a gift of the Almighty. What you lost is gone to the Almighty. You came empty-handed and will go empty handed only. The balance will be nil. What you possess now once belonged

to somebody else, and will be possessed by somebody else in future. Don't be attached to that. Attachment is the root cause of worries.

- Change is the law of nature. Take yourself as a millionaire for a while and the very next moment will make you weep. Just give up the notions of mine, yours, high, lows, etc. and you will see that everything is yours.

- Neither this body belongs to you, nor do you belong to the body. Everything is made up of 5 elements—earth, water, air, fire and vacuum. But the soul is eternal. Then what are you?

- Devote yourself to the Almighty. Learn to count upon Him and then see how fear, worry, sorrow, etc. disappear for ever.

- Whatever you do, dedicate it to the Almighty. It will lead you to the salvation as a cakewalk.